S0-AGI-732

Chemistry SL

Alexandra Juniper
Jason Murgatroyd

International Baccalaureate
Baccalauréat International
Bachillerato Internacional

IB Prepared
Approach your exams the IB way
Chemistry SL

Published January 2011

International Baccalaureate
Peterson House, Malthouse Avenue, Cardiff Gate
Cardiff, Wales GB CF23 8GL
United Kingdom
Phone: +44 29 2054 7777
Fax: +44 29 2054 7778
Website: http://www.ibo.org

The International Baccalaureate (IB) offers three high quality and challenging educational programmes for a worldwide community of schools, aiming to create a better, more peaceful world.

IB merchandise and publications can be purchased through the IB store at http://store.ibo.org. General ordering queries should be directed to the sales and marketing department in Cardiff.

Phone: +44 29 2054 7746
Fax: +44 29 2054 7779
Email: sales@ibo.org

British Library Cataloguing in Publication Data.
A catalogue record for this book is available from the British Library.

ISBN: 978-1-906345-38-9

Cover design by Pentacor**big**
Typeset by Wearset Ltd
Printed and bound in Spain by Edelvives

International Baccalaureate, **Baccalauréat International** and **Bachillerato Internacional** are registered trademarks of the International Baccalaureate Organization.

Item code 4051
2015 2014 2013 2012 2011
10 9 8 7 6 5 4 3 2

Acknowledgments
Gareth Hegarty and Brian Murphy for advice on IB Diploma Programme chemistry standard level

IB learner profile

The aim of all IB programmes is to develop internationally minded people who, recognizing their common humanity and shared guardianship of the planet, help to create a better and more peaceful world.

IB learners strive to be:

Inquirers
They develop their natural curiosity. They acquire the skills necessary to conduct inquiry and research and show independence in learning. They actively enjoy learning and this love of learning will be sustained throughout their lives.

Knowledgeable
They explore concepts, ideas and issues that have local and global significance. In so doing, they acquire in-depth knowledge and develop understanding across a broad and balanced range of disciplines.

Thinkers
They exercise initiative in applying thinking skills critically and creatively to recognize and approach complex problems, and make reasoned, ethical decisions.

Communicators
They understand and express ideas and information confidently and creatively in more than one language and in a variety of modes of communication. They work effectively and willingly in collaboration with others.

Principled
They act with integrity and honesty, with a strong sense of fairness, justice and respect for the dignity of the individual, groups and communities. They take responsibility for their own actions and the consequences that accompany them.

Open-minded
They understand and appreciate their own cultures and personal histories, and are open to the perspectives, values and traditions of other individuals and communities. They are accustomed to seeking and evaluating a range of points of view, and are willing to grow from the experience.

Caring
They show empathy, compassion and respect towards the needs and feelings of others. They have a personal commitment to service, and act to make a positive difference to the lives of others and to the environment.

Risk-takers
They approach unfamiliar situations and uncertainty with courage and forethought, and have the independence of spirit to explore new roles, ideas and strategies. They are brave and articulate in defending their beliefs.

Balanced
They understand the importance of intellectual, physical and emotional balance to achieve personal well-being for themselves and others.

Reflective
They give thoughtful consideration to their own learning and experience. They are able to assess and understand their strengths and limitations in order to support their learning and personal development.

Table of contents

1. Introduction

As an IB student, you are provided with many resources on the path to your final chemistry standard level (SL) exams. This book is just one of the resources to help you prepare.

How to use this book

Welcome to IB Prepared!

Although the advice in this book can be very helpful in preparing for an exam the IB way, it cannot replace nearly two years of content learning. So use this book as a **supplement** to your classroom experience and not as a replacement.

The main function of this book is to help you prepare for your exams. It includes advice on how to approach exam questions. Real exam questions are followed by actual IB student answers. These are accompanied by senior examiner commentary highlighting how marks were gained (☺) and lost (☹), with suggestions for how students might have improved their answers. We suggest that, before you read the students' responses, you should try to answer the questions by yourself.

What is in this book?

- **Chapter 2** explains the **command terms**. These are key words used in exam questions that tell you what is expected in your written answers.

- **Chapter 3** focuses on the **structure of the exam papers**. Included in this is an overview of paper 3 and questions with model answers on each option.

- **Chapter 4** provides top tips. These are pieces of **general advice and strategies** that have been created as a result of reviewing the reports written by examiners (the people who mark your exams).

- **Chapters 5–15** have been broken up to match the **syllabus topics** you are taught.

  - The first half of each chapter contains different topics sections. First it identifies key concepts (through "You should know" and

"You should be able to") as well as common pitfalls in sections entitled "Be prepared". It then lists any definitions you should know. We have only provided a selection of these—there are many more that you will be expected to know. This section also includes some examples of how the topic content may appear in multiple-choice questions, or short-answer questions, followed by some advice on how to answer them.

  - The second half of each chapter gives examples of the questions you may face in your exams. We have chosen a mix of questions from paper 2 for each section of the syllabus. Questions are provided to show you the range of possible questions, and then actual student answers are shown. For each answered question, we

provide examples of a range of performance—these are actual answers, written by IB students like you. The exam questions are accompanied by suggestions to help you approach the question and should only be used as guidance. To help you gain an insight into the way examining works, for each answer we provide you with the mark that was given and an explanation, written by a senior examiner, of strengths and weaknesses in the student response. (Be aware that, in some instances, we have only used parts of questions, and not complete questions.)

- Last, in **chapter 16**, you will find a complete set of papers from May 2010, allowing you to put in to practice what you have learned from this book.

2. Command the command terms

In this chapter you will gain an understanding of command terms (action verbs) and how they relate to exam questions.

Understanding the command terms is the key to making sure that you answer the question asked in sufficient depth and get all of the marks available for the question. The command terms themselves reflect what IB examiners believe a student ought to be able to achieve after completing the course. Below are some of the common command terms used in chemistry and an explanation of what some of them mean. They have not all been explained in detail, as there are 30 in total—and the book would become very long if we included them all! So if you come across one not explained here, then look at your syllabus or ask your teacher to explain what it means.

The first group of command terms is designed to allow you to show your basic competence in demonstrating your knowledge of methods, concepts, facts and so on—these are objective 1. The second group of terms tests your ability to apply this knowledge—objective 2. The third group allows you to show how well you can analyse and evaluate scientific ideas and how easily you can construct new links—objective 3.

Assessment objective group 1

The command terms from this group are: **define, draw, label, list, measure** and **state**. These terms test your factual knowledge. Examiners will want to see an ability to recall standard facts and ideas. Here are four commonly used terms in chemistry.

Define
This means that you need to give a definition, an exact description of what the word means. Throughout the book you will find lots of definitions—study them and learn them!
For example (from topic 2, atomic structure):

- **Define** the terms mass number (A), atomic number (Z) and isotopes of an element.

State
A very brief answer will suffice without the need for any explanation.
For example (from topic 2, atomic structure):

- **State** the position of protons, neutrons and electrons in the atom.

Draw
Draw using a pencil, and a ruler, if necessary.
For example:

- **Draw** the isomers of C_4H_{10}.

or

- **Draw** the Lewis structure of CO_2.

Label
For this you will need to **label** a diagram you have drawn or one that is on the exam paper. It is important that you make it clear what your labels refer to.

Assessment objective group 2

The second group of command terms requires you to apply your knowledge. The terms in this category are **annotate**, **apply**, **calculate**, **describe**, **distinguish**, **estimate**, **identify** and **outline**. All of these terms are used in chemistry questions, although the following are the most commonly used.

Calculate   This means that you need to work something out and find the answer to a question. It is important that you always show your working in these questions so that, if you make a mistake with your arithmetic, you can still get marks for your method.

For example:

- **Calculate** the relative atomic mass of magnesium if the isotopic abundances are 77.3% ^{24}Mg, 12.1% ^{25}Mg and 10.6% ^{26}Mg. Give your answer to 2 dp.

The answer (including working) is

$$\frac{(24 \times 77.3) + (25 \times 12.1) + (26 \times 10.6)}{100} = 24.333 = 24.33 \text{ to 2 dp}$$

In this case, 1 mark is available for the calculation method and 1 mark for having the answer to the correct number of decimal places.

Describe   This is very commonly used in chemistry questions and it is important that you include sufficient detail in your answers.

Here are some examples of the use of **describe** in the syllabus.

- **Describe** the ionic bond as the electrostatic attraction between oppositely charged ions.

- **Describe** how ions can be formed as a result of electron transfer.

This is an example of the use of **describe** in a question on bonding.

- The elements sodium, aluminium, silicon, phosphorus and sulfur are in period 3 of the periodic table.

Describe the metallic bonding present in sodium and aluminium.

The answer will be that there are delocalized electrons, which are attracted to the positive metal ions, creating the metallic bond.

Outline   This is a frequently used command term, especially in paper 3. The term **outline** is used when a brief account is required or a summary of the points in an argument. A detailed explanation is not required and it is often a good idea to answer this sort of question using bullet points.

Assessment objective group 3

The third group of command terms requires you to use high-order skills of analysis and evaluation in using your chemistry. The terms in this category are **analyse**, **comment**, **compare**, **construct**, **deduce**, **derive**, **design**, **determine**, **discuss**, **evaluate**, **explain**, **predict**, **show**, **sketch**, **solve** and **suggest**. Some of these are used far more frequently than others in chemistry.

Explain

Explain requires more than a description or an outline—it requires you to **explain** why something is happening. For example:

- The equation for the reaction between methane and chlorine is

$$CH_4(g) + Cl_2(g) \rightarrow CH_3Cl(g) + HCl(g)$$

Explain why no reaction takes place between methane and chlorine at room temperature unless the reactants are sparked, exposed to UV light or heated.

To answer this, you have to **explain** that the molecules have insufficient energy to react at room temperature because the collisions are not sufficiently energetic to cause the bonds to break, and that adding energy via a spark or UV light will supply the extra energy needed to overcome the activation energy for the reaction.

Discuss

Discuss has a similar meaning to **explain**, but you may be asked to compare alternatives or to give views for or against an argument. This sort of question requires careful planning and thought before writing begins, to ensure that you give a balanced view.

Determine

Determine essentially means **work out**, and has a similar meaning to **calculate** in chemistry. Often you will be using numbers to find an answer.

For example:

- The relative molecular mass of aluminium chloride is 267 and its composition by mass is 20.3% aluminium and 79.7% chlorine. **Determine** the empirical and molecular formulas of aluminium chloride.

Here, by dividing the percentages given by the relative atomic masses, and then finding the ratio of moles, you find out that the empirical formula is $AlCl_3$. To work out the molecular formula, you divide the molecular mass by the mass of the empirical formula, $n = \dfrac{267}{133.5} = 2$, so the molecular formula is Al_2Cl_6.

Deduce

Deduce has a similar meaning to **determine**, as you need to work something out, but you must show a justification for your answer.

Compare

This command term requires you to look at more than one piece of information and to draw out similarities and differences. It is essential that when you see the term **compare** you ensure that you do refer to the things you are comparing and include similarities **and** differences so you do not lose marks.

Sketch

When you see the command term **sketch** it is not necessary to use graph paper. However, make sure that the axes of your graph are labelled and that you include appropriate units, if this is applicable. For example, you could be asked to sketch the Maxwell–Boltzmann distribution.

Combining the command terms

Sometimes, the command terms are grouped together.

For example:

- **State** and **explain two** methods, other than measuring pH, which could be used to distinguish between $1.0\,mol\,dm^{-3}$ solutions of nitric acid and ethanoic acid.

To answer this, you must **name two** methods and then **explain** why they both work. So a possible answer would be as follows.

1. Conductivity—because nitric acid will contain more ions and have a higher conductivity than ethanoic acid, which will have fewer ions and have a lower conductivity.

2. Rate of reaction with magnesium—nitric acid will react more rapidly and produce bubbles of hydrogen faster than ethanoic acid.

The important thing is to remember to include both parts of the answer when you are in the exam room. Think of the different command terms as distinct. If you cannot answer the higher-order part of the question, make sure that you do as much as you can of the easier part.

3. Get to know your exam paper

This chapter aims to explain the structure of the exam you will be sitting and the details regarding each of its parts, so as to give you an overall view of the exam and a few general guidelines that should help you prepare for the different papers.

General

- The final grade you will get in chemistry will depend on how well you do in your internal assessment (practical work), which contributes 24% of the final grade, and on how well you do in the three papers you sit that form the external exam and contribute the other 76%. Below is a summary of the external assessment.

Paper	Length (minutes)	Marks available	Percentage of final grade
1	45	30	20
2	75	50	32
3	60	40	24

- Paper 1 is multiple-choice and is 45 minutes long. After this exam, you will sit paper 2 straight afterwards, and it is 1 hour and 15 minutes long. The next morning you will sit paper 3, which is 1 hour long.

- For papers 1 and 2 you will need to know all of the core chemistry from the syllabus—so syllabus topics 1–11. In paper 3 you need to know your two options really well.

- In papers 2 and 3 you must be careful, as it is possible to lose 1 mark for too few or too many significant figures (abbreviated to sig. fig. or sf) and also 1 mark for incorrect or missing units (abbreviated to U). Potentially this is 4 marks in total. Also, in some questions, you can be asked to record to a particular number of decimal places or work out a unit, and there are then additional marks for this skill. See "Top tips" for help on this.

Paper 1

- This is a multiple-choice paper with 30 questions in 45 minutes, which averages out at 1.5 minutes per question—some questions will take longer and some are relatively quick to answer, but you do need to work through these quickly. Whatever else happens, you must complete the paper and give a response to all 30 questions—even if it is a guess, there is a 25% chance of getting it right. (If you put nothing, it will be 100% wrong!)

- All questions have four possible answers (A, B, C and D) and you need to answer in pencil by shading in a rectangle on a grid corresponding to A, B, C or D—make sure you have an HB pencil, a sharpener and eraser.

- You cannot use a calculator for paper 1. Although all the calculations are quite straightforward, you need to practise not reaching for your calculator every time you see a number in a question! The calculations are designed to be done using simple mental arithmetic, often involving multiplication or division by numbers such as 2 or 5 or powers of 10.

- You also do not have access to a chemistry data booklet, although you will have a copy of the periodic table inside the front cover on page 2.

- To tackle the questions, look carefully at the question and make sure you know what it is asking, and underline the key words. Then it is usually possible to reject some of the answers quite quickly. Put a cross next to these. Then you can focus on the possible correct answers. If you are still not sure, then leave it blank and come back to it at the end, and choose between the answers you are left with—remember to put something down.

- Often, all the answers look as if they might be correct, but you are asked to choose the **best** answer.

- A small number of questions, usually between three and six in SL paper 1, are multiple completion, which means that there are three possible options (I, II and III) to consider, and either two or three of these are correct. You must then answer according to the following scheme.

Answer	Choices
A	I and II only
B	I and III only
C	II and III only
D	I, II and III

- There will be questions on all 11 topics, and the number of questions on each topic will be roughly in proportion to the number of suggested teaching hours. This means that there will be more questions on topic 4 (bonding), which has 12.5 hours, than on topic 2 (atomic structure), which has 4 hours.

- Common examples of what the questions test are facts, definitions, explanations, trends in properties, or simple calculations—the questions will test objectives 1 and 2.

- Remember that you can do your working on the question paper, as this will not be sent in.

The following illustrates types of multiple-choice questions that you could come across.

Which compound has the empirical formula with the largest mass?

A. C_2H_6

B. C_2H_4

C. C_2H_2

D. C_3H_6

This might seem like a calculation, but it is not really. You first need to know what an empirical formula is, then convert each formula from molecular to empirical—which gives CH_3, CH_2, CH and CH_2. You could then work out the "mass" of each of these using values from the periodic table. However, each empirical formula has one carbon atom, so the one with the most hydrogen atoms must be the answer, CH_3. So you should choose A.

Which is the best description of ionic bonding?

A. The electrostatic attraction between positively charged nuclei and an electron pair

B. The electrostatic attraction between positive ions and delocalized negative ions

C. The electrostatic attraction between positive ions and delocalized electrons

D. The electrostatic attraction between oppositely charged ions

All the answers look possible at first.

A is a good description of the force of attraction in covalent bonding.

B is almost correct, except for the inclusion of "delocalized".

C is a good description of metallic bonding.

D is the correct answer.

Which process represents the C—Cl bond enthalpy in tetrachloromethane?

A. $CCl_4(g) \rightarrow C(g) + 4Cl(g)$

B. $CCl_4(g) \rightarrow CCl_3(g) + Cl(g)$

C. $CCl_4(l) \rightarrow C(g) + 4Cl(g)$

D. $CCl_4(l) \rightarrow C(s) + 2Cl_2(g)$

Choosing the right answer involves knowing the precise meaning of bond enthalpy—it refers to the breaking of one bond in the gaseous state. So, in this case, you could start by eliminating C and D because they are not all in the gaseous state. Then A is eliminated because four bonds are broken, which leaves B as the right answer—one bond broken and everything in the gaseous state.

According to the collision theory, which factors affect reaction rate?

I. The state of the reactants
II. The frequency of the collisions between particles
III. The average kinetic energy of the particles

A. I and II only

B. I and III only

C. II and III only

D. I, II and III

This is an example of the multiple completion type. It is sometimes possible to get questions like this correct even if you do not know whether one of the statements is correct or not, but you are sure about one or two of them. For example, if you were sure that I was definitely wrong, then the answer would have to be C, or if II was definitely wrong, then the answer would have to be B. However, in this case, all the statements are correct, so the answer is D.

Paper 2

- This paper consists of two sections.
  - Section A has 30 marks distributed over several structured questions, and all parts are compulsory.
  - Section B has 20 marks for one extended-response style question, and you pick one extended-response question out of three. How you choose is crucial.

- Before paper 2 you have 5 minutes reading time—use it to read over the whole paper, starting with section A. Your brain will get to work looking for things straight away. When you get to section B, you need to read each question thoroughly. Quite often, if you read the first section of the question only, you will get a nasty shock further down. Once reading time is over, you are allowed to write. At this point, go through the questions in section B, marking down next to each sub-question how many marks you think you can achieve. Choosing the wrong question in section B can dramatically affect your grade, and so spending time on it is well worthwhile.

- Now you are ready to start the paper, and again every mark has 1.5 minutes allocated. Start where you are most confident—this could be section A or one of the extended-response questions, but you need to watch the clock. A sensible timing is 40 minutes in section A and 25 minutes on the extended-response question, which then leaves you 10 minutes to check over everything—units, significant figures, equations and so on.

- You also are allowed to use a calculator and the chemistry data booklet—make sure you know what information you can find in it.

- Half the marks will be objective 1 and 2, and the other half will be objective 3 marks that will often require a more detailed answer and/or a greater level of understanding.

- As well as the example here, there are lots of examples of paper 2 questions in the following chapters.

- In paper 2 you will need to answer data-analysis type questions, and you may be asked to comment on a hypothesis. The following questions illustrate how this may look in an exam paper.

2. Alex and Hannah were asked to investigate the kinetics involved in the iodination of propanone. They were given the following equation by their teacher.

$$CH_3COCH_3(aq) + I_2(aq) \xrightarrow{\;H^+(aq)\;} CH_2ICOCH_3(aq) + HI(aq)$$

Alex's hypothesis was that the rate will be affected by changing the concentrations of the propanone and the iodine, as the reaction can happen without a catalyst. Hannah's hypothesis was that as the catalyst is involved in the reaction, the concentrations of the propanone, iodine and the hydrogen ions will all affect the rate.

They carried out several experiments varying the concentration of one of the reactants or the catalyst whilst keeping other concentrations and conditions the same. Their results are shown graphically below.

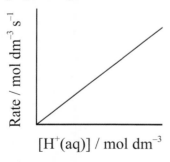 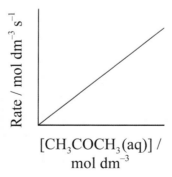 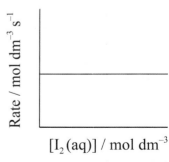

(a) Discuss whether either Alex's or Hannah's hypothesis is correct. [2]

By looking at the graphs, you can see that changing the concentration of iodine does not affect the rate of reaction. This means that neither of the hypotheses is completely correct. Hannah is right about H⁺ and propanone, and wrong about iodine. Alex is wrong about both iodine and H⁺.

- Some questions will be asked to test your wider knowledge of how chemistry relates to environmental, ethical or economic issues. There may be several correct answers to questions like these, and you should be aware of where they occur in the syllabus. One example is given below, and others are included in the following chapters.

(iii) Outline why the polymerization of alkenes is of economic importance and why the disposal of plastics is a problem. *[2]*

There are several possible answers to this question. Reasons for economic importance are that plastics are cheap or versatile, or that it is a very large industry and plastics have many uses. The disposal problems are caused because plastics are not biodegradable and they can take up a lot of space in landfill as they do not decompose.

Paper 3

- To prepare for this paper, you need to know your two options in detail, and you should look carefully at the syllabus. In the syllabus you will see a column called objectives (obj), and 50% of paper 3 (and paper 2) should be objective 3 type questions. Therefore, topics that are objective 3 are more likely to be asked—use this to help target your revision. Also, just because something has not

been asked before does not mean that it will not be asked in the future. So do not be tempted to leave things out.

- In this paper you will answer questions on two out of a possible seven options, A–G, that you would have studied. You must answer questions on only two of them.
- The options often have a lot of factual content, but the papers are going to test the chemistry behind these facts as well, so make sure you really understand the chemical basis of what you are learning so that you can explain and apply it.
- When answering paper 3 you are allowed a calculator and the data booklet, and it is a good idea to study what is in the data booklet so you can easily find information in the exam.
- Again there are 1.5 minutes per mark, so 30 minutes maximum per option, but you must check over things like units, significant figures, equations and so on. Also you will have five minutes reading time, so read over both options carefully to start your brain processing.

In the rest of this chapter there are selections of questions from the May 2009 papers for each option. As you study only two out of the seven possible options, we have not gone into a great deal of detail for each option. After each question there are some guiding questions (**these are in blue**) that will help you to understand how to approach the question, what skills you need and what areas of the syllabus it links to. After this, there is a model answer written by an examiner (**this is in black**).

Option A: Modern analytical chemistry

(c) The following diagram represents a thin-layer chromatogram of an amino acid.

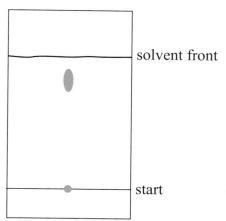

(i) Outline the principle of thin-layer chromatography. Refer in your answer to the nature of the mobile and stationary phases and the reason why a mixture of amino acids can be separated using this method. *[2]*

(ii) State **one** advantage of thin-layer chromatography over paper chromatography. *[1]*

(iii) Calculate the R_f of the amino acid. *[1]*

You need to have a good understanding of how chromatography is used to separate and identify substances in mixtures, and in this case the use of thin-layer chromatography. The question says outline, so you do not need lots of detail other than what is specified in the question. Also, as there are 2 marks available, you need to make at least two valid points for (ii).

(i) The stationary phase is a thin layer of silicon dioxide or aluminium oxide and the mobile phase is a solvent.

A mixture of amino acids is separated because each amino acid will bond more or less to the stationary phase depending on the functional groups it contains.

(ii) Separation with thin-layer chromatography is more efficient and effective than with paper chromatography.

(iii) The R_f value is given by

$$R_f = \frac{\text{distance travelled by sample}}{\text{distance travelled by solvent}} = \frac{40}{46} = 0.87$$

A2. Mass spectrometry is a powerful analytical technique used in the identification of organic compounds. The mass spectrum of a compound with empirical formula CH_2O displays peaks at *m/z* 15, 45 and 60.

(a) Determine the molecular formula of the compound. *[1]*

(b) Identify the fragments responsible for the peaks at *[2]*

m/z = 15

m/z = 45

(c) Identify a compound that could produce this spectrum. *[1]*

You need to understand mass spectrometry and the use of m/z values to identify a compound, remembering that the highest mass will be the mass of the molecular ion. Also remember that all fragments carry a positive charge, as otherwise they would not be detected.

(a) The largest mass is 60, so this is the mass of the molecular ion. The empirical formula CH_2O has a mass of 30, so the molecular formula is twice that, $C_2H_4O_2$.

(b) The value m/z = 15 could be CH_3^+ and m/z = 45 could be $COOH^+$.

(c) A compound that could produce this spectrum would be ethanoic acid, CH_3COOH.

A3. Infrared spectroscopy is an analytical technique that uses electromagnetic radiation.

(a) Compare infrared radiation and visible light in terms of the processes that occur in atoms and molecules upon absorption. *[2]*

(b) Explain at the molecular level why oxygen molecules do not absorb infrared radiation. *[2]*

The first part requires an understanding that infrared radiation has less energy than visible light, and for this reason the effect the radiation has on atoms is distinct. Infrared radiation can cause bending and stretching of bonds, whereas visible light can cause electrons to move from one shell to another, which requires more energy.

(a) Infrared radiation would cause bonds to stretch and bend. The visible light would allow electrons to be promoted to higher energy levels within the atom.

To answer the second part of the question, you must remember that, for absorption of infrared to occur, there must be a change in dipole moment when a bond stretches or bends.

(b) At a molecular level, oxygen molecules are symmetrical and non-polar. If oxygen bonds bend and stretch, there is no change in dipole moment, so infrared radiation is not absorbed.

Option B: Human biochemistry

B3. Vitamins are micronutrients essential for good health.

(a) Compare the solubilities of vitamins A and C in water by referring to the structures provided in Table 21 of the Data Booklet. *[2]*

(b) Describe the effect of deficiency of **one** of these vitamins and suggest **two** possible solutions. *[3]*

(c) Steroids and phospholipids are both classes of lipid found in the body. Cholesterol is a steroid. A structure of lecithin, a phospholipid, is shown below.

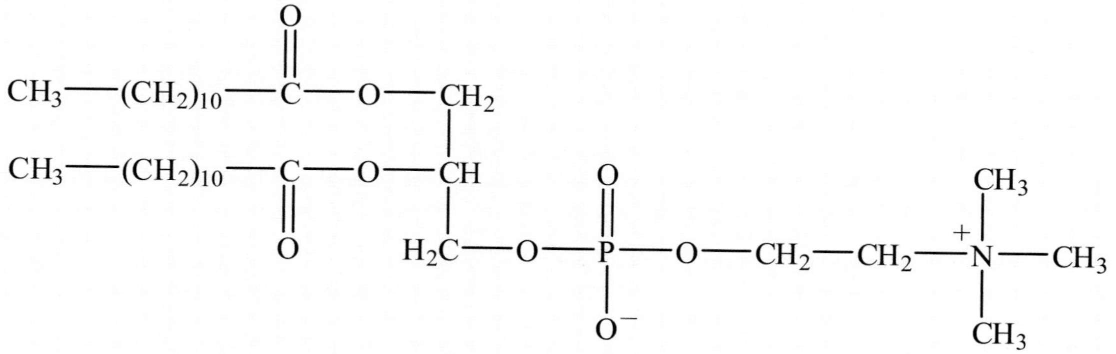

(i) Distinguish between *HDL* and *LDL* cholesterol. *[2]*

(ii) Compare the composition of cholesterol with a phospholipid such as lecithin. *[1]*

(iii) Determine whether cholesterol or lecithin is more soluble in water. *[1]*

You must understand how molecular structure will influence solubility. The structures of the vitamins are in table 21 of the data booklet and you should be familiar with them. Molecules with several —OH groups can hydrogen bond with water, and so the molecule is water soluble. Long hydrocarbon chains are not polar and are not soluble in water.

Here you can talk about vitamin C and scurvy or vitamin A and night blindness. You then need to suggest two possible solutions to vitamin deficiency, which could be in terms of the diet you need to follow or the vitamin enrichment of foods.

(a) Vitamin A will not dissolve in water because it has a long non-polar hydrocarbon chain. Vitamin C will dissolve in water because it contains several —OH groups, which means it can hydrogen bond to water.

(b) A deficiency of vitamin C will lead to scurvy. Two possible solutions to this vitamin deficiency are to eat more fresh fruit and vegetables that contain vitamin C, and to add extra vitamin C to fruit juices or food.

(i) This question requires you to distinguish between HDL and LDL cholesterol, which means you need to compare them and explain how they are different.

(i) LDL is a larger molecule than HDL. LDL is formed from saturated fats and is associated with transporting cholesterol to the arteries, whereas HDL is formed from unsaturated fats and is associated with removing cholesterol from the arteries.

(ii) Here you must compare the composition of cholesterol and a phospholipid, so you need to look at what they are made of and mention both in your answer.

Cholesterol contains the elements C, H and O, whereas lecithin contains C, H, O, N and P.

(iii) To decide on this, you need to look at the functional groups in cholesterol and lecithin to decide which would be more polar and most able to hydrogen bond. Since it says determine, there should be some reasoning with your answer.

Lecithin will be more soluble because it has ionic charges, which means that it is more polar.

Option C: Chemistry in industry and technology

C1. Alloys are important substances in industries that use metals.

(a) Describe an alloy. *[1]*

(b) Explain how alloying can modify the structure and properties of metals. *[2]*

(c) Describe the effect of the *tempering* process on steel. *[1]*

(d) Discuss the environmental impact of iron and aluminium production. *[2]*

(a) This question requires recall of the composition of an alloy as a homogeneous mixture.

An alloy is a homogeneous mixture of a metal with another metal or non-metal.

(b) In this question, you must explain how alloying can change the structure of the metal, as the atoms have a different size, and how this then amends the properties, as layers cannot slide over each other. In this question, you could include diagrams to help you explain.

In an alloy the added atoms (metal or non-metal) are of a different size to the metal atoms and so disrupt the metal lattice. This means that the layers of metal atoms can no longer slide over each other. This will mean the metal is much less malleable and so is more brittle and harder.

(c) This requires recall of what the tempering process does in steel making.

The tempering process is used to make steel less brittle.

(d) Since this is a discuss question, it will be necessary to come up with a range of points that include the environmental impact of aluminium production and the environmental impact of iron production. However, as there are only 2 marks available, it should not be necessary to say a lot.

The manufacture of iron and aluminium releases large quantities of CO_2 into the atmosphere partly because of the large quantity of energy needed for the processes. This is leading to global warming. Mining leads to scarring of the landscape and also can produce slag heaps of waste.

C3. The high activity of lithium metal leads to the formation of an oxide layer on the metal which decreases the contact with the electrolyte in a battery.

(a) Describe how this is overcome in the lithium-ion battery. *[2]*

(b) Describe the migration of ions taking place at the two electrodes in the lithium-ion battery when it produces electricity. *[2]*

Anode (–):

Cathode (+):

(c) Discuss **one** similarity and **one** difference between fuel cells and rechargeable batteries. *[2]*

Similarity:

Difference:

(a) To answer this question, you need to describe how the composition of the lithium-ion battery removes the problem caused by lithium metal oxidizing.
The battery does not contain lithium metal, which would oxidize. Instead, it contains lithium ions dissolved in an organic solvent, which acts as an electrolyte. It is the lithium ions that then move between the electrodes.

(b) Here you are asked to describe the migration of ions taking place at the electrodes. You can answer this sort of question with the relevant equations, which you need to learn in this topic.
At the anode: oxidation occurs, electrons are released and

$$LiC_6 \rightarrow Li^+ + 6C + e^-$$

At the cathode: reduction occurs, electrons are accepted and

$$Li^+ + e^- + MnO_2 \rightarrow LiMnO_2$$

(c) *Here, discuss one similarity and one difference means that there will be more than one acceptable answer. You should suggest a similarity between the fuel cell and the rechargeable battery, which could be that both are electrochemical cells. A difference would be that in a rechargeable battery the redox processes that happen can be reversed whereas in a fuel cell they cannot.*

A similarity is that they both involve spontaneous redox reactions, which convert chemical energy directly to electrical energy.

A difference is that a battery is a device that stores energy, whereas a fuel cell is a device that only converts energy—it does not have a store of chemical energy like a battery, and so needs a constant supply of reactants to work.

Option D: Medicines and drugs

D1. Medicines and drugs can influence the functioning of the body.

Discuss the term *therapeutic window*. Your answer should include its meaning, a quantitative description and an explanation of **wide** and **narrow** therapeutic windows. *[4]*

Since this question asks you to discuss, you will need to break it down into parts, and use the prompts you are given in the question. You need to include the meaning of the term "therapeutic window", as well as a description using a mathematical expression. You also have to explain what "wide" and "narrow" therapeutic windows are and how this is related to the way the drug is used.

The term "therapeutic window" is used to describe the relative margin of safety of a drug. It is defined as LD_{50}/ED_{50}, or the

lethal dose for 50% of the population divided by the effective dose for 50% of the population.

A wide therapeutic window means that the lethal dose is high and the effective dose is small, so a large amount of the drug can be taken before the drug becomes toxic. A narrow therapeutic window means that the amount taken must be very carefully controlled, as an effective dose will be very close to being a lethal dose, so there is a much lower margin of safety.

D3. Ethanol, a depressant, is sufficiently volatile to pass into the lungs from the bloodstream. The roadside breathalyser test uses acidified potassium dichromate(VI) which reacts with any ethanol present in the breath and converts it to ethanoic acid.

(a) (i) State the oxidation and reduction half-equations that occur in the breathalyser when ethanol is present in the breath. *[2]*

Oxidation:

Reduction:

(ii) Describe the colour change that occurs to the acidified dichromate(VI) if ethanol is present in the breath. *[1]*

(b) Police use the intoximeter, an infrared spectrophotometer to confirm a roadside breathalyser test. Explain how the amount of ethanol is determined from the infrared spectrum. *[2]*

(a) (i) *You need to write the equations for both the oxidation and reduction reactions that occur in a breathalyser when ethanol is oxidized by potassium dichromate(VI) (the equation with dichromate is in table 14 of the data booklet). Since they are separate half-equations, you do not need to balance them with each other.*

The oxidation of ethanol:

$$C_2H_5OH + H_2O \rightarrow CH_3COOH + 4H^+ + 4e^-$$

The reduction of dichromate:

$$Cr_2O_7^{2-} + 14H^+ + 6e^- \rightarrow 2Cr^{3+} + 7H_2O$$

(ii) *This requires simple recall of the colour change of orange to green that you should know from organic chemistry.*

The colour will change from orange to green, showing the reduction of the dichromate (VI) ion.

(b) *This requires you to have a good understanding of how the intoximeter works, as you have to explain how the amount of alcohol in the breath is worked out from the degree of* absorption in the infrared spectrum by the C—H bond in ethanol.

The intoximeter will show an absorption for both the O—H bond and the C—H bond in the gases in the breath. Since O—H is in water, it is the C—H bond that is used to measure the amount of ethanol. This is done by measuring the amount of absorption and comparing it to known samples. If there is a greater absorption, then there is more alcohol in the breath.

Option E: Environmental chemistry

E3. The ozone in the stratosphere protects us from harmful UV radiation. Above Australia there is an area of decreased ozone concentration that has led to an increase in the incidence of some skin cancers.

   (a) Write equations for the natural formation of ozone. [2]

   (b) Discuss the advantages and disadvantages of using hydrocarbons in place of CFCs. [2]

(a) *Here you are asked for the equations for the formation of ozone, so you need to recall how UV light breaks an oxygen molecule into two free radicals and how the free radicals then join with oxygen.*

$$O_2 \rightarrow 2O\cdot \text{ and } O\cdot + O_2 \rightarrow O_3$$

(b) *Here you are asked to discuss advantages and disadvantages, so to get both marks you must make at least one suggestion for an advantage and one for a disadvantage.*

Hydrocarbons do not contain weak C—Cl bonds, so are not going to be ozone-depleting, which is an advantage. However, hydrocarbons are flammable, which is a disadvantage.

E2. Water purity is often assessed by reference to its oxygen content.

   (a) Outline the meaning of the term *biochemical oxygen demand* (BOD). [2]

   (b) Describe how the dissolved oxygen concentration in a river would decrease if

      (i) a car factory releases warm water into the river after using it for cooling. [1]

      (ii) a farmer puts large quantities of a fertilizer on a field next to the river. [1]

(a) *You are asked to outline the meaning of the term BOD. It is a definition you are being asked for, and you should have spent time studying this so you can recall it in the exam. It is worth 2 marks, so your answer will need to be detailed. A mark will be for explaining BOD and another mark for the conditions it is measured under.*

The biological oxygen demand is the amount of oxygen needed to decompose the organic matter in a sample of water at 20°C over a period of 5 days.

(b) (i) *You are asked to describe how the oxygen decreases when warm water is put into the river, which is why it is important that you understand the chemical processes that* are occurring. In this case it is that gas solubility in water decreases with increasing temperature.

The oxygen level decreases because oxygen is less soluble in hot water.

(ii) *You are asked to describe how the oxygen decreases when fertilizers are put on a field next to the river, and again it is important that you understand the chemical processes that are occurring. In this case it is eutrophication you need to describe.*

The oxygen level would decrease because the fertilizer would go into the river and cause the algae to grow much more. This would lead to an algal bloom and eventual eutrophication.

Option F: Food chemistry

F1. (a) Describe the chemical composition of a triglyceride. *[1]*

(b) The following two structures represent isomers of a fatty acid.

State and explain which isomer has the higher melting point. *[3]*

(a) You are asked to describe the chemical composition of a triglyceride, so your answer should include the substituents it is made up of and the class of compounds it belongs to—it is an ester.

A triglyceride is an ester formed by glycerol reacting with three fatty acid molecules. It is composed of C, H and O.

(b) To answer this, you must remember that melting point is dependent on the strength of the intermolecular forces between molecules. When you look at the isomers, you must choose which has the strongest intermolecular forces and hence the higher melting point and explain why this is so. In this case the trans isomer II has the greater surface area, so stronger van der Waals' forces.

Isomer II, which is the trans isomer, will have the higher melting point. This is because in II the isomer has a larger surface area—the cis isomer I is much more compact. This means that isomer II has much greater van der Waals' forces between the molecules, which leads to a higher melting point.

F3. Genetically modified (GM) foods are now widely available, although in some countries environmental groups are campaigning against them. Define the term *genetically modified food* and discuss the benefits and concerns of using GM foods. *[5]*

To answer this question successfully, you need to structure your answer well to get the 5 marks available. First you must define the term "genetically modified food". Then you are asked to discuss benefits and concerns. Your answer will need to include both benefits and concerns and preferably at least two of each.

A genetically modified food is something that has been produced from a genetically modified organism.

The **benefits** of using GM foods are numerous, because we can produce food that has a higher nutritional quality, and also a food that tastes and looks better. GM foods can also be produced in larger quantities, as they can be modified to be resistant to pests and disease.

The **concerns** are that there could be a link to increased allergies in people, and also that GM organisms could affect ecosystems and this could lead to the extinction of native species.

Option G: Further organic chemistry

G1. Benzene is an important molecule containing delocalized electrons.

    (a)   Explain the term *delocalized electrons*.   *[1]*

    (b)   State and explain **one** piece of physical evidence and **one** piece of chemical evidence for the presence of delocalized electrons in the structure of benzene.   *[4]*

    (c)   Describe and explain the relative rates of the reactions of hydroxide ions with chlorobenzene, C_6H_5Cl, and (chloromethyl)benzene, $C_6H_5CH_2Cl$.   *[3]*

(a) In this question you need to explain that delocalized electrons are not localized to one particular bond between two atoms but are distributed over three or more adjacent atoms.

Delocalized electrons are electrons that are not held in a bond between two atoms but electrons that are spread over three or more atoms.

(b) There are 4 marks available for this question, and to get all of them you need to structure your answer well. You are asked to state and explain one piece of physical evidence, which could be bond length, electron density and so on, and to state and explain one piece of chemical evidence, which could be that benzene reacts by substitution rather than addition or the fact that the enthalpy of hydrogenation is less than it would be for cyclohexatriene. Cyclohexatriene also has the molecular formula C_6H_6 but it has three double and three single bonds and so would behave very differently from benzene.

One piece of physical evidence is that when the C—C bond lengths are measured in benzene they are all the same length, and this length is between a single and double bond length. This happens because the electrons are delocalized over the ring and there are not alternating single and double bonds.

One piece of chemical evidence is that the enthalpy of hydrogenation of benzene

$$C_6H_6 + 3H_2 \rightarrow C_6H_{12}$$

is not just three times the enthalpy of hydrogenation of cyclohexene

$$C_6H_{10} + H_2 \rightarrow C_6H_{12}$$

This is because benzene is more stable than the theoretical cyclohexatriene, because of the delocalization, so less energy is evolved when it is hydrogenated.

(c) In this question you need to describe the relative rates of hydrolysis of chlorobenzene and (chloromethyl)benzene, and then explain why (chloromethyl)benzene reacts faster, as it is reacting via a nucleophilic substitution on the side chain as opposed to an electrophilic substitution into the ring.

The rate of hydrolysis of (chloromethyl)benzene is faster. This is because in (chloromethyl)benzene the chlorine being substituted is attached to a carbon that is not part of the ring, so the C—Cl bond is weaker and easier to break. In chlorobenzene the chlorine is attached directly to the ring and a lone pair of its electrons is involved in the delocalized ring of electrons. As well as making the C—Cl bond stronger, this makes the C—Cl bond in chlorobenzene less polarized and less attractive to nucleophiles.

G2. (a)   Magnesium is a very electropositive metal which can be used in the formation of Grignard reagents.

        (i)   State the product when bromomethane and magnesium react together in a non-polar solvent.   *[1]*

        (ii)   Draw the structural formulas of the organic products formed in the following reactions.   *[2]*

$$CH_3CH_2MgBr \xrightarrow[H_2O]{CO_2}$$

$$CH_3CH_2MgBr \xrightarrow[H_2O]{(CH_3)_2CO}$$

(i) *You are asked to state the product, which is methyl magnesium bromide, or CH_3MgBr. It does not matter if you use a name or a formula here.*

The product will be CH_3MgBr, methyl magnesium bromide.

(ii) *Here you need to draw the structural formulas of the products of the reactions—names would not be sufficient here. In the first case MgBr is replaced by CO_2, leading to the formation of propanoic acid. In the second case 2-methylbutan-2-ol forms when MgBr is replaced by $(CH_3)_2CO$. If you run out of time and do not put all the hydrogen atoms in the structures, then you would lose 1 mark.*

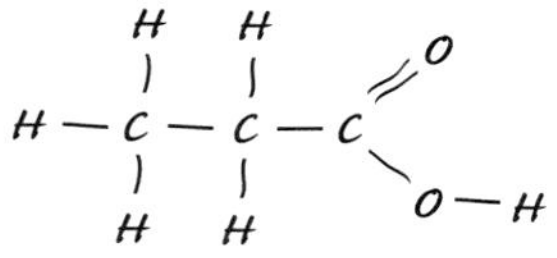

CH_3CH_2COOH

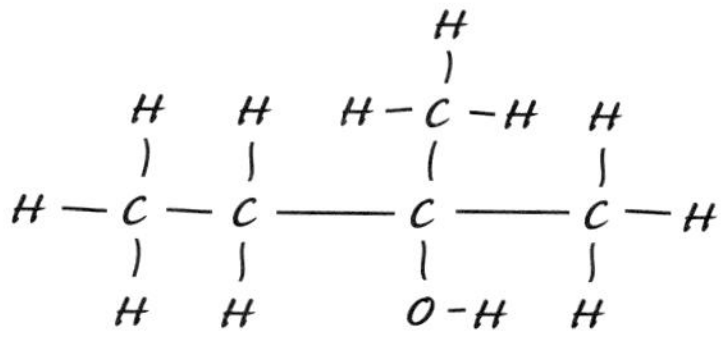

$CH_3CH_2C(CH_3)(OH)CH_3$

Here are some tips that will help you throughout your exams. Some of them may be obvious, but these are sometimes the ones that students forget!

Revision strategies

- Gather your resources, including the subject guide (containing the assessment statements of the syllabus), your notes, your course text and past papers and their markschemes. **Past papers are available for purchase from http://store.ibo.org.**

- Start by reviewing what you knew well earlier but may have forgotten since you last studied it.

- Next learn material that is straightforward but that you never found the time to learn solidly up until now.

- Do some past multiple-choice papers and consult the answers as a diagnostic tool to determine your areas of strength and weakness. **Remember that only multiple-choice papers from May 2009 onwards are relevant for the current syllabus**.

- Begin to revise the syllabus comprehensively, point by point.

- If you have studied more than two options, you are advised to concentrate on just the two you will answer in the exam.

Data booklet

- In the paper 2 and 3 exams (but not in paper 1), you should have a copy of the chemistry data booklet with you, and you should get to know its contents during the course. You should check that you have the most recent edition—it should say "First examinations 2009" on the front and "Revised edition published September 2008" on the inside. You will probably be loaned one for the exam, just in case you have written anything in your own copy that you should not have access to in the exam room.

- When you use the periodic table in table 5 for relative atomic masses, you should always include the two decimal places shown when doing calculations.

- Some questions will include a reference to a table in the data booklet, but other questions expect you to realize that you must get information from it.

Marking principles

It will help you to do well in the exams if you know something about the instructions given to markers.

- **The list principle**. This means that if you are asked for **two** answers, for example, in a question, then you should **only** give two answers. If you give more than two, then if the extra answers are correct, they will score no more marks, but if the extra answers are wrong, then you will lose marks. For example, a question based on assessment statement 9.5.4 might be "State the products obtained during the electrolysis of molten sodium chloride". The correct answer is sodium (at the negative electrode) and chlorine (at the positive electrode).

This answer might be worth 1 mark, but say it was 2 marks. The answer "sodium, chlorine and hydrogen" contains one wrong and two right answers, and would score only 1 mark. The answer "sodium, chlorine, hydrogen and oxygen" contains two wrong and two right answers and would score no marks.

- **Spelling and punctuation.** Ideally these would be completely correct, but they are not as important as the actual chemistry content. You are not likely to lose a mark if you write feenolfthaleen instead of phenolphthalein because the wrong spelling sounds just like the correct one and it cannot be confused with another substance you should know about. However, if you write ethane instead of ethene when the answer should be the name of the alkene, then your answer will be marked wrong because ethane and ethene are different substances.

- **Names and formulas.** If you are asked for the name of a substance, then the formula will not be marked right, and a name instead of a formula will also not score. If the question asks you to identify a substance, then either a correct name or a formula will score.

Question	Acceptable	Unacceptable
State the name of the alkene containing two carbon atoms.	ethene	C_2H_4
Give the formula of the nucleophile used to convert bromoethane to ethanol.	OH^-	hydroxide ion
Identify the catalyst used in the manufacture of ammonia	iron / Fe	

- **Contradictions.** If you mention something in an answer that contradicts a correct statement you have made, then you may lose marks. A common topic in which this occurs is bonding, where you have to be careful to use the terms atom, ion and molecule in the right contexts. The same is true for covalent, ionic and metallic bonds and intermolecular forces. For example, if you were writing about the bonding in silicon dioxide, you would probably score a mark for mentioning the covalent bonds between the atoms. But, if you later in the same answer write something like "the intermolecular forces are strong" or "the ions are strongly attracted to each other", then you would probably lose the previous mark for covalent bonding. This is because covalent bonds and ionic bonds and

intermolecular forces are very different, and an answer that mixes them up shows a serious lack of understanding (or perhaps an attempt to include all types of bonding because one of them must be right!).

Calculations

You are more likely to score full marks in calculations if you follow this advice.

- Set out the calculation clearly, so that your working can be followed. In many calculations marks can be awarded even if your answer is wrong, provided that you have used a correct method. Often it is a good idea to underline the final answer. In some calculations it helps to add just a few words of explanation to show what you are doing—these could be used to award method marks.

- Sometimes you are given the units to use for the final answer, but even if not, you should always include them with your answer.

- Pay attention to significant figures, and make sure you know the difference between significant figures (sig. fig. or sf) and decimal places (dp). The following examples should help you.

	Significant figures	Decimal places
25.65	4	2
0.1	1	1
0.100	3	3
53475	5	0
0.003	1	3
0.025	2	3

The best advice is that you should give your final answer to the same number of significant figures as the data in the question. If the data varies in the number of significant figures, then you should give your answer to the smallest number of significant figures used. You may be penalized for an inappropriate number of significant figures in a final answer.

- Remember the principle of consequential marking, sometimes called "error carried forward" or "follow-through" marks. This means that in a calculation with several steps, if you get an intermediate answer wrong, you will lose marks. However, if you then use that wrong answer in a correct method in a later step, you will continue to score marks, even though your final answer will be different from the one in the markscheme.

Syllabus and markschemes

Having your own copy of the syllabus is a very good idea. You can use it to check that you have covered everything you should know, and the "Teacher's notes" column gives you even more detail about what could be asked in the exam. In chemistry (more so than in some other subjects) the markers use detailed markschemes to guide them in awarding marks. Your teacher should be able to provide you with recent examples of markschemes. You should find them very useful in getting to know the level of detail you need to give for full marks in questions.

- Each marking point begins on a separate line. The end of the marking point is shown using a semicolon (;).

- An alternative answer or wording is indicated in the markscheme by showing it after a "/". This means that either wording can be accepted. Examiners will not look for exactly the words quoted in the markscheme but will allow the idea however expressed.

- Underlined words or phrases are, however, compulsory and the mark will not be given unless the word, phrase or idea is present.

- Words in brackets (…) in the markscheme are not required to gain the mark, but clarify matters for the examiners.

- The order of points does not have to be as written (unless stated otherwise).

Symbols, formulas and equations

- Take care when writing symbols (for example, for chlorine write Cl and not CL or cl).

- Avoid careless errors when writing formulas (for example, write CO_2 and not CO2 or Co_2).

- Equations should always be balanced for the number of atoms on each side, and if there are ions included, then they should be balanced for charge as well. This is shown by these examples.

Unbalanced	$CH_4 + O_2 \rightarrow CO_2 + H_2O$
Balanced	$CH_4 + 2O_2 \rightarrow CO_2 + 2H_2O$

Unbalanced	$MnO_4^- + H^+ \rightarrow Mn^{2+} + H_2O$
Balanced except for charge	$MnO_4^- + 8H^+ \rightarrow Mn^{2+} + 4H_2O$
Balanced	$MnO_4^- + 8H^+ + 5e^- \rightarrow Mn^{2+} + 4H_2O$

- When writing equations for reversible reactions (for example, the dissociation of a weak acid), use the reversible arrow symbol.

Incorrect	$CH_3COOH \rightarrow CH_3COO^- + H^+$
Correct	$CH_3COOH \rightleftharpoons CH_3COO^- + H^+$

- For information about the different types of formula used for organic compounds, look at assessment statement 10.1.3 in the syllabus.

Organic reaction mechanisms

Most of these involve drawing curly arrows to represent the movement of electron pairs. Many students find it difficult to draw these accurately, so here is a brief guide to the main examples. Every arrow should start from a pair of electrons (either from a bond line or a lone pair) and point to the final location of the pair of electrons. There are only three types of mechanism included in the Core, with others included in Option G of paper 3. Those that are **only** in Option G are identified in the following examples.

- One example is from a nucleophile to another atom and forming a bond between the nucleophile and the atom (strictly speaking, the arrow should point to the mid-point of the new bond, but this is never insisted on).

- (Option G) A second example is from one bond line to another bond line and forming a second bond (and so giving a double bond).

- A third example is from a bond line to an atom and forming a negative ion.

- (Option G) A fourth example is from a bond line to a positive ion and forming a bond with the ion.

- When the arrow starts from a nucleophile, it should start from a lone pair of electrons, although credit may be given if it starts from the atom with the negative charge or from the negative charge itself. For example, when the nucleophile is the hydroxide ion, the arrow should start from the lone pair of electrons on O. Credit may be given if the arrow starts from O or from the negative charge, but not if it starts from the H atom.

Correct   Acceptable   Wrong

- In S_N2 mechanisms, the transition state should be shown with dashed lines for two of the bonds (the one being formed and the one being broken), with square brackets, and with the negative charge outside the square brackets. Ideally, the two dashed lines should be opposite to each other (at 180°).

- In free-radical mechanisms it is possible to show the movement of a single electron by a half-arrow (sometimes called a fish-hook), but the IB does not expect these.

- When showing a radical, it is good practice to show a dot to represent the unpaired electron, although the IB does not insist on these.

$$CH_3 \cdot$$

Don't forget …

- Write clearly and use black or dark blue ink for your answers. (Do not use red ink.)

- If a question asks you to sketch a graph, you should do this in pencil in the space provided and not on a separate sheet of graph paper.

- If you are asked to give a colour change, then you should give two colours—the original and final colours.

- When writing organic formulas and structures, be careful to show the bonds correctly between the right atoms. Here are some examples.

Acceptable	Not acceptable
$HO-CH_2-CH_2-OH$	$OH-CH_2-CH_2-OH$
$H_2N-CH_2-CH_2-NH_2$	$NH_2-CH_2-CH_2-NH_2$
$HOOC-CH_2-CH_2-COOH$	$COOH-CH_2-CH_2-COOH$

- The use of "stick" formulas, with bonds shown but missing hydrogen atoms, should be avoided, as shown by this example.

Acceptable

Unacceptable

- The number of answer lines provided for a question part is meant to suggest the amount of space for the expected answer, although some students write answers that are longer than the space provided. Such students should complete their answers in the white space below the lines if possible, and not write a few words on a continuation sheet. If they must use continuation sheets in this way, then they should indicate in the booklet that the particular answer is continued elsewhere. Continuation sheets should really be used only in section B of paper 2.

- Use scientific language, not journalistic language, when describing or explaining things. Here are some examples.

Recommended	Not recommended
penicillin-resistant bacteria	superbugs
beneficial bacteria	friendly bacteria
low density	light
infrared radiation from the Earth is absorbed by carbon dioxide molecules and radiated back to the Earth's surface	heat rays from the Earth bounce off the carbon dioxide and go back to the Earth

21

5. Quantitative chemistry

The mole concept and Avogadro's constant

You should know:

- the mole (mol) can be considered as a collection containing a very large number of objects (6.02×10^{23} to be precise), in the same way that one dozen is a collection of 12 objects

- the mole can apply to particles, atoms, ions and so on (or even bananas!)

- Avogadro's constant (L) is $6.02 \times 10^{23}\,\text{mol}^{-1}$, and there are this number (6.02×10^{23}) of atoms, ions and so on in one mole.

You should be able to:

- use the mole concept and Avogadro's constant to calculate the number of particles or amount of substance.

Be prepared

- Always work out questions from first principles and write out all steps. It is very easy to go wrong with a question by missing out a step.

- Use the triangle

where N = number of atoms, n = amount in moles and L = Avogadro's constant.

Example

How many ions are there in 0.10 mol of copper(II) nitrate?

One mole of anything is Avogadro's number, 6.02×10^{23},

so 0.1 mol will be $0.1 \times 6.02 \times 10^{23} = 6.02 \times 10^{22}$.

Then work out the formula of copper(II) nitrate.

The ions are Cu^{2+} and NO_3^-, so the formula is $Cu(NO_3)_2$.

So in the formula there are 3 ions in total,

so $3 \times 6.02 \times 10^{22} = 18.06 \times 10^{22} = 1.8 \times 10^{23}$ (to 2 sf)

Formulas

You should know:

- the definitions of relative atomic mass (A_r) and relative molecular mass (M_r)

- an empirical formula is the simplest ratio of the atoms of each element in a compound

- a molecular formula is the actual number of atoms of each element in a compound.

You should be able to:

- calculate the amount of substance in moles (mol), molar mass (mass of one mole) in $g\,mol^{-1}$ and mass in g, if given sufficient information

- calculate both empirical and molecular formulas from given data.

Be prepared

- Use the triangle

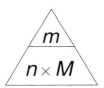

where n = amount in mol, m = mass in g and M = molar mass in $g\,mol^{-1}$.

- Always set out your working for an empirical formula in a table.

Key definitions

- Relative atomic mass, A_r, is the average mass of one atom of the element compared to $\frac{1}{12}$ of the mass of an atom of ^{12}C.

- Relative molecular mass, M_r, is the sum of the average masses of the atoms in the molecule compared to $\frac{1}{12}$ of the mass of an atom of ^{12}C.

Example

(a) Determine the empirical formula of a hydrocarbon that is comprised of 85.6% carbon and 14.4% hydrogen.

Since 85.6% plus 14.4% equals 100%, there is nothing else in the compound. The percentages can be converted to grams, so that 85.6 g of C are combined with 14.4 g of H.

	Carbon	Hydrogen
Mass (g)	85.6	14.4
Molar mass ($g\,mol^{-1}$)	12.01	1.01
$\dfrac{Mass}{Molar\ mass}$	7.13	14.3
Ratio	7.13/7.13 = 1	14.26/7.13 = 2
Formula	C	H_2

Empirical formula is CH_2.

(b) If the molar mass of the compound is $70.2\,g\,mol^{-1}$, what is its molecular formula?

CH_2 has a mass of $(1 \times 12.01) + (2 \times 1.01) = 14.03$,

so $\dfrac{70.2}{14.03} = 5$

Therefore the molecular formula is 5 times CH_2 and is C_5H_{10}.

Chemical equations

You should know:

- the symbols of the elements
- state symbols: solid (s), liquid (l), gas (g) and aqueous solution (aq), which means dissolved in water.

You should be able to:

- balance chemical equations using whole numbers
- identify mole ratios of reactants and/or products in a chemical equation
- distinguish between coefficients (large numbers in front of formulas) and subscripts (small numbers within formulas).

Be prepared

- A coefficient goes in front of a formula.

- The formula should never be changed to balance the equation.

Example

Write a balanced equation including state symbols for the reaction between aqueous solutions of sulfuric acid and sodium hydroxide.

The balanced equation is

$$H_2SO_4(aq) + 2NaOH(aq) \rightarrow Na_2SO_4(aq) + 2H_2O(l)$$

First, it was necessary to write the correct formulas of the reactants and products. Then the 2 is placed before sodium hydroxide and water to balance the equation. Last, the state symbols are included. Note that, when it forms, water is a liquid and not aqueous.

Mass and gaseous volume relationships in chemical reactions

You should know:

- the theoretical yield is the maximum amount of product that can be made and is often different from the experimental yield
- Avogadro's law states that one mole of any gas will occupy the same volume if the temperature and pressure are the same
- at standard temperature and pressure, STP (273 K and 101 kPa), the molar volume is $2.24 \times 10^{-2}\,m^3$ ($22.4\,dm^3$).

You should be able to:

- identify the limiting reactant in an equation, usually by working out which reactant is in excess (some of this reactant will be left over)
- solve problems using the ideal gas equation, $PV = nRT$.

Be prepared

- Accurate A_r values from the data booklet should always be used to calculate M_r values.
- $PV = nRT$ can be used to solve problems with gases and you can find it in the data booklet.
- When dealing with gases, always use the temperature in kelvins, which is °C + 273.
- Use $\dfrac{P_1 V_1}{T_1} = \dfrac{P_2 V_2}{T_2}$ to solve simple problems when one variable is changing.

Example

A mass of 4.38 g of calcium carbonate was added to $100\,cm^3$ of $0.500\,mol\,dm^{-3}$ hydrochloric acid. The equation for the reaction that occurs is

$$CaCO_3(s) + 2HCl(aq) \rightarrow CaCl_2(aq) + H_2O(l) + CO_2(g)$$

(a) Determine the limiting reactant.

M_r of $CaCO_3$ is $40.08 + 12.01 + (3 \times 16.00) = 100.09$, so $n(CaCO_3) = 4.38 \div 100.09 = 0.0438\,mol$

$n(HCl) = 0.100 \times 0.500 = 0.0500\,mol$ (to 3 sf), so HCl is the limiting reactant.

Although the amount of $CaCO_3$ is less than that of HCl, the equation shows that they react in a 1:2 ratio. This means that $0.0250\,mol$ of $CaCO_3$ reacts with $0.500\,mol$ of HCl. So, as there is $CaCO_3$ left over at the end of the reaction, then HCl is the limiting reactant.

(b) Calculate the volume of carbon dioxide produced, measured at 20°C and $1.02 \times 10^5\,Pa$.

The equation shows that the mole ratio for HCl and CO_2 is 2:1, and HCl is the limiting reagent, so

$n(CO_2) = \frac{1}{2}n(HCl) = 0.0500 \div 2 = 0.0250\,mol$

$PV = nRT$

So $V = nRT \div P = (0.0250 \times 8.31 \times 293) \div (1.02 \times 10^5)$
$= 5.97 \times 10^{-4}\,m^3$

Here we have converted from the Celsius scale to the Kelvin scale and our answer is in m^3.

Or $V = nRT \div P = (0.0250 \times 8.31 \times 293) \div (1.02 \times 10^2)$
$= 5.97 \times 10^{-1}\,dm^3$

Here we have converted from the Celsius scale to the Kelvin scale, converted Pa to kPa and our answer is in dm^3.

Solutions

You should know:

- the solute is the substance that dissolves
- the solvent is a liquid that dissolves the solute
- a solution forms when a solute dissolves in a solvent
- concentration depends on the amount of solute dissolved and can be measured in $g\,dm^{-3}$ and $mol\,dm^{-3}$.

You should be able to:

- solve problems using
$$\text{concentration } (mol\,dm^{-3}) = \frac{\text{amount (mol)}}{\text{volume of solution } (dm^3)}.$$

Be prepared

- Remember that when calculating the volume of solution, volume should be in dm^3 to match the concentration units of $mol\,dm^{-3}$.
- cm^3 can be converted to dm^3 by dividing by 1000.
- Use the triangle

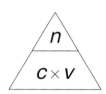

where n = amount in mol, c = concentration in $mol\,dm^{-3}$ and v = volume in dm^3.

Example

In a titration, $25.0\,cm^3$ of phosphoric acid was placed in a conical flask with a suitable indicator. It was found that $29.4\,cm^3$ of $0.150\,mol\,dm^{-3}$ sodium hydroxide was needed for complete reaction according to this equation:

$$3NaOH(aq) + H_3PO_4(aq) \rightarrow Na_3PO_4(aq) + 3H_2O(l)$$

Calculate the concentration, in $g\,dm^{-3}$, of the phosphoric acid.

$n(NaOH) = 0.150 \times 0.0294 = 0.00441\,mol$

Since the reacting ratio is 3 : 1,

then $n(H_3PO_4) = 0.00441 \div 3 = 0.00147\,mol$

Concentration of H_3PO_4 is $0.00147 \div 0.0250 = 0.0588\,mol\,dm^{-3}$

M_r of H_3PO_4 is $(3 \times 1.01) + 30.97 + (4 \times 16.00) = 98.0$

So concentration in $g\,dm^{-3}$ is $0.0588 \times 98.00 = 5.76\,g\,dm^{-3}$.

3. Smog is common in cities throughout the world. One component of smog is PAN (peroxyacylnitrate) which consists of 20.2 % C, 11.4 % N, 65.9 % O and 2.50 % H by mass. Determine the empirical formula of PAN, showing your working. *[3]*

[Taken from paper 2, time zone 2, May 2009]

How do I approach the question?

Calculations of empirical formulas need to be carefully set out—perhaps using a table, but at least using a column for each element. Keep the elements in the same order as given in the question.

Remember to divide the percentage figure by the A_r value taken from the data booklet. It is good practice to use the actual values in the data booklet and not round them to the nearest whole number, although in this type of calculation no marks would be deducted for using whole-number values.

Do not stop after you have found the ratio of whole numbers—use them to write the empirical formula.

In some questions (not this one), the sum of the percentage figures does not add up to 100 because the figure for one element has been deliberately left out (usually oxygen). In these cases the question should contain words such as "… the remainder being oxygen".

Consider the 3-mark allocation. In this question the first mark is for showing that the correct method is for dividing the percentage values by the appropriate relative atomic masses and successfully completing the calculations, the second mark is for dividing by the smallest value to give a whole-number ratio, and the third mark is for a correct final answer.

What are the key areas of the syllabus?

- Calculation of empirical formula from experimental data.

This answer achieved 0/3

Although the student has set out the calculation neatly and obtained a final answer, a completely wrong method has been used. Instead of dividing the percentage figures by the A_r values, the division has been done the wrong way round. This is a serious error in the method, so even though the arithmetic is correct, no marks can be awarded.

C	N	O	H	
$\frac{12}{20.2}$	$\frac{14}{11.4}$	$\frac{16}{65.9}$	$\frac{1}{2.5}$	0/1
0.59	1.23	0.24	0.4	
3	6	10	2	0/1
Formula is $C_3N_6O_{10}H_2$				0/1

This answer achieved 2/3

The student has set out the calculation neatly and used the correct method, with a few helpful words to explain each step. Although the final ratio is correct, for some reason the subscript 3 for H has been left out, so the last mark is lost.

	C	N	O	H	
$\frac{\%}{A_r}$	$\frac{20.2}{12}$	$\frac{11.4}{14}$	$\frac{65.9}{16}$	$\frac{2.5}{1}$	1/1
ratio	1.68	0.814	4.12	2.5	
or	2	1	5	3	1/1
Empirical formula is C_2NO_5H					0/1

This answer achieved 3/3

Although the student has not used any words of explanation, the calculation has been set out neatly using the correct method (dividing the percentage figure by the relative atomic mass for each element, then working out the simplest whole-number ratio) and a correct final answer is written.

C	N	O	H	
$\dfrac{20.2}{12}$	$\dfrac{11.4}{14}$	$\dfrac{65.9}{16}$	$\dfrac{2.5}{1}$	1/1
1.68	0.81	4.12	2.5	
2	1	5	3	1/1
$C_2NO_5H_3$				1/1

(b) A student reacted some salicylic acid with excess ethanoic anhydride. Impure solid aspirin was obtained by filtering the reaction mixture. Pure aspirin was obtained by recrystallization. The following table shows the data recorded by the student.

Mass of salicylic acid used	3.15 ± 0.02 g
Mass of pure aspirin obtained	2.50 ± 0.02 g

(ii) Calculate the theoretical yield, in g, of aspirin, $C_6H_4(OCOCH_3)COOH$. *[2]*

(ii) Calculate the theoretical yield, in g, of aspirin, $C_6H_4(OCOCH_3)COOH$. *[2]*

(iii) Determine the percentage yield of pure aspirin. *[1]*

[Taken from paper 2, time zone 2, May 2009]

How do I approach the question?

(i) The amount of substance is calculated by dividing the mass in grams by the relative formula mass of the substance (which you have to work out using the relative atomic mass values from table 5 of the data booklet). Although it is good practice to include the unit "mol", you do not have to here because this question includes the words "in mol".

(ii) You need to check the mole ratio for the salicylic acid and aspirin reaction. As there are no coefficients in the equation (the complete equation, using structural formulas, was given in the question), the ratio is 1 : 1. This means that the same amount (in moles) of aspirin will be formed as the amount of salicylic acid you calculated in (i). To get the answer in grams, you have to multiply the amount by the relative formula mass of aspirin (which again you have to work out using table 5 of the data booklet).

(iii) The percentage yield of a product is worked out by dividing the actual yield (your theoretical yield answer from (ii)) by the actual mass obtained (in the table in the question) and multiplying by 100.

How do I approach the question?

- Calculating M_r from A_r values
- Considering mole ratios in equations
- Understanding the different terms involving yield (experimental, theoretical, percentage) and knowing how to use them in calculations

This answer achieved 2/5

The correct answer is 0.0228 mol, so the student's answer is 10 times bigger than it should be. As there is no working shown, no mark can be awarded for a method.

(i)   amount = 0.228 moles   0/2

(ii)   same amount of aspirin formed (M_r = 180) so yield is
       180 × 0.228 = 41.04 g   2/2

(iii) yield = $\frac{41.04}{2.50}$ = 16.4%   0/1

This answer is 10 times bigger than it should be, but that is because of the mistake made in the previous part. As the correct method has been used, full marks have been awarded. This is a good example of an error carried forward. If a wrong answer is correctly used later in the question, full marks can still be scored in later parts.

The division is the wrong way round, and there is no multiplication by 100.

This answer achieved 3/5

Although the M_r is correct and a correct method has been used, the wrong figure has been copied from the table in the question (2.50 should be 3.15).

(i) M_r of salicylic acid = (7 × 12) + (3 × 16) + (6 × 1) = 138

       moles = $\frac{2.50}{138}$ = 0.0181   1/2

(ii)   the yield is 176 × 0.0181 = 3.19 g   1/2

(iii) yield = $\frac{2.50 \times 100}{3.19}$ = 78.4%   1/1

Again, a correct method has been used, but there is another mistake here—the M_r of aspirin is wrong (it should be 180). The error carried forward principle has been used to award 1 mark for the correct method.

Although the answer is not the one in the markscheme, the correct method has been used, the error carried forward principle has been applied and there are no further mistakes.

This answer achieved 5/5

The formula mass is correct, and to two decimal places using the values from the data booklet, and the amount in moles has been calculated using the right method.

The theoretical yield expression is the right one and the correct answer has been obtained by substituting the right values of the formula mass of aspirin and the amount in moles from the previous part.

The percentage yield expression correctly shows the division of the actual mass obtained by the theoretical yield and multiplication by 100.

(i) The formula mass of salicylic acid
$$= (7 \times 1.01) + (3 \times 16.00) + (6 \times 1.01) = 138.13$$
$$number\ of\ moles = \frac{3.15}{138.13} = 0.0228 \qquad 2/2$$

(ii) theoretical yield is number of moles of aspirin × formula mass of aspirin
$$= 180.17 \times 0.0228 = 4.11 g \qquad 2/2$$

(iii) percentage yield $= \frac{2.50 \times 100}{4.11} = 60.8\%$ $\qquad 1/1$

---

1. A 0.265 g sample of a mixture of calcium chloride, $CaCl_2$, and potassium nitrate, KNO_3, is dissolved in 50.0 cm^3 of water. This mixture is titrated with 0.100 mol dm^{-3} silver nitrate, $AgNO_3$, which reacts with the chloride ions present to form insoluble silver chloride, $AgCl$. The titration required 38.5 cm^3 of silver nitrate.

   (a) Write an equation for the reaction between calcium chloride and silver nitrate. *[2]*

   (b) Calculate the amount, in moles, of silver nitrate used in the reaction. *[2]*

   (c) Calculate the amount, in moles, of calcium chloride titrated and the mass of calcium chloride present in the original sample. *[3]*

   (d) Calculate the percentage of calcium chloride in the original sample. *[1]*

[Taken from paper 2, time zone 1, May 2008]

How do I approach the question?

(a) The formulas of the two reactants have been given, but you need to work out the formula of the second product (you are given the formula of silver chloride) and then to balance the equation. The 2-mark allocation is because 1 mark is for formulas and 1 mark for balancing.

(b) You need to calculate the amount by multiplying the volume by the concentration, remembering that the volume must be converted to dm^3 (this is to match the concentration in mol dm^{-3}).

(c) You need to remember to check the mole ratio for $CaCl_2$ and $AgNO_3$ from the equation you wrote in part (a), before multiplying the amount by the relative formula mass of calcium chloride.

(d) This is a straightforward percentage calculation. You need to divide the mass of calcium chloride from (c) by the mass given in the question and multiply by 100.

What are the key areas of the syllabus?

- Calculating M_r from A_r values

- Considering mole ratios in equations

- Using the two expressions involving amounts in moles (one also involves volume and molar concentration, the other involves mass and relative formula mass)

5. Quantitative chemistry

This answer achieved 2/8

Although the formulas of the reactants have been correctly copied from the question, the product formulas are wrong. Even though the equation appears to be balanced (it has the same number of each atom on both sides), marks are never awarded for balancing an equation using wrong formulas.

Although the student knows that the amount of a compound in solution should be calculated by multiplying the volume by the molar concentration, the volume should have been divided by 1000, so the answer is 1000 times too big.

(a) $CaCl_2 + AgNO_3 \rightarrow AgCl_2 + CaNO_3$ 0/2

(b) moles of $AgNO_3 = 0.100 \times 38.5 = 3.85$ 1/2

(c) moles of $CaCl_2 = 3.85$

so mass of $CaCl_2 = 3.85 \times (40 + 70) = 423.5\,g$ 1/3

(d) $\% = \frac{423.5}{0.265} = 1598\%$ 0/1

 There is a missing 100 from the calculation.

The student may have used the 1 : 1 mole ratio from the equation written in (a), or the mole ratio may not have been considered and the value just copied from (b). Another mistake is to use the wrong relative atomic mass values. It is always good practice to use the values from the periodic table in the data booklet, but rounding them to the nearest whole number is **sometimes** acceptable. In this case, the value for calcium has been rounded down from 40.08 to 40, which is acceptable. The value for chlorine should **never** be rounded to a whole number (but 35.5 is often acceptable).

This answer achieved 5/8

The reactant formulas and the $CaCl_2$: $AgNO_3$ mole ratio are correct, although the formula of calcium nitrate is wrong and the equation is not balanced.

A correct mole calculation has been carried out using the concentration and volume values from the question.

The student has not used the 1 : 2 mole ratio from the equation written in (a), although the relative atomic masses and the calculation are correct.

(a) $CaCl_2 + 2AgNO_3 \rightarrow 2AgCl + 2CaNO_3$ 0/2

(b) moles of $AgNO_3 = \frac{0.100 \times 38.5}{1000} = 0.00385$ 2/2

(c) moles of $CaCl_2 = 0.00385$

so mass of $CaCl_2 = 0.00385 \times (40.08 + 2 \times 35.45) = 0.4273\,g$ 2/3

(d) $\% = \frac{0.4273 \times 100}{0.265} = 161.2\%$ 1/1

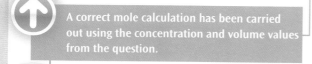 The calculation has been correctly done and the error carried forward principle has been used to award the mark for an answer not in the markscheme. Note that, even though an impossible percentage (more than 100%) has been given, this can still score marks. However, if there is time, the student should realize that this is an impossible answer and go through the question again to see if the mistake can be spotted.

This answer achieved 7/8

The student has correctly multiplied the concentration and volume to get the amount in moles.

All formulas are correct and the equation is balanced.

The student has used the 1:2 mole ratio from the equation written in (a) the wrong way round, although the mass calculation has used the correct method.

The student has correctly multiplied the concentration and volume to get the amount in moles.

(a) $CaCl_2 + 2AgNO_3 \rightarrow 2AgCl + Ca(NO_3)_2$ 2/2

(b) amount of $AgNO_3$ = 0.100 × 0.0385 = 0.00385 mol   2/2

(c) amount of $CaCl_2$ = 0.00385 × 2 = 0.00770
so mass of $CaCl_2$ = 0.00770 × (40.08 + 70.90) = 0.8545 g   2/3

(d) $\% = \dfrac{0.8545 \times 100}{0.265} = 322.45\%$ 1/1

6. Atomic structure

Atoms, isotopes and the mass spectrometer

You should know:

* the details about subatomic particles given in the table

Subatomic particle	Relative mass	Relative charge	Position in atom
Proton	1	+1	In nucleus
Neutron	1	0	In nucleus
Electron	5×10^{-4}	−1	In energy levels (shells) orbiting nucleus

* a mass spectrometer is used to determine relative atomic masses by comparing the masses of atoms to the mass of ^{12}C

* the main stages in the operation of a mass spectrometer are: Vaporization, Ionization, Acceleration, Deflection and Detection (VIADD).

You should be able to:

* work out which isotope is present from the mass and atomic numbers

* calculate the number of protons, neutrons and electrons in atoms and ions

* work out the relative atomic mass given the masses and abundances of isotopes

* compare the properties of isotopes—remember that chemical properties are the same and physical properties vary.

Be prepared

* You should be able to describe the use of radioisotopes such as ^{14}C, ^{60}Co, ^{131}I and ^{125}I.

Key definitions

* Mass number (A) = the number of protons and neutrons in an atom.

* Atomic number (Z) = the number of protons in an atom (also equal to the number of electrons in an atom).

* Isotopes are atoms of the same element with the same atomic number but different mass numbers.

Example

Consider the composition of the species W, X, Y and Z below. Which species is an anion?

Species	Number of protons	Number of neutrons	Number of electrons
W	9	10	10
X	11	12	11
Y	12	12	12
Z	13	14	10

A. W

B. X

C. Y

D. Z

Answer W.

Here the answer must be W, as anions carry a negative charge, and as this is the only species where the number of electrons is greater than (>) the number of protons. The number of neutrons is irrelevant in this case.

Electron arrangement

You should know:

- ultraviolet (UV) light has a higher frequency and shorter wavelength than visible light

- visible light has a higher frequency and shorter wavelength than infrared (IR) light

- a continuous spectrum will contain all possible wavelengths of light within a range

- a line spectrum only contains single (discrete) lines

- lines converge towards high frequency.

You should be able to:

- draw an energy level diagram to show the transitions between energy levels in an atom

- explain that lines in the emission spectrum relate to these energy level transitions

- work out the electron arrangement of atoms, for example Na is (2,8,1).

Be prepared

- The data booklet contains the equations $E = hf$ and $c = f\lambda$, which you can use to answer questions.

Example

(a) State the electron arrangement of the following species: P^{3-}.

The arrangement is 2,8,8.

Phosphorus has 15 electrons (Z = 15) and, because the species has a 3⁻ charge, it has gained three electrons. The species has 18 electrons in total, and these 18 electrons are arranged in three levels/shells.

(b) Energy levels for an electron in a hydrogen atom are

A. evenly spaced.

B. farther apart near the nucleus.

C. closer together near the nucleus.

D. arranged randomly.

Here the answer is B.

You need to remember that the energy levels (electron shells) are further apart at the nucleus and get closer together as you get further away from the nucleus—this is called convergence.

5. (a) (i) Describe and explain the operation of a mass spectrometer.   [5]

    (ii) State **three** factors that affect the degree of deflection of ions in a mass spectrometer.   [3]

    (iii) Strontium exists as four naturally-occurring isotopes. Calculate the relative atomic mass of strontium to two decimal places from the following data.   [2]

Isotope	Percentage abundance
Sr-84	0.56
Sr-86	9.90
Sr-87	7.00
Sr-88	82.54

[Taken from paper 2, time zone 1, May 2009]

How do I approach the question?

(i)   You need to know how the mass spectrometer works. **Describe** suggests that you should say what the processes are, and **explain** suggests that you should say how they are made to happen. The one most students overlook is how detection works. The 5-mark allocation suggests that five processes should be included.

(ii) An understanding of how deflection works is needed, so as to identify exactly what the factors are. The 3-mark allocation confirms the need to state three factors.

(iii) For each isotope you need to multiply the mass number and abundance together, then add the results together. If percentages are given in the question, then division by 100 is needed.

What are the key areas of the syllabus?

- The working of a mass spectrometer

- The calculation of relative atomic masses from data (including percentage abundances)

This answer achieved 3/10

The student's brief answer is a list and not a description or explanation and does not cover any of the points in the markscheme, so does not score any marks.

Both speed and mass are correct answers, but the number of electrons has been ignored as it is not relevant. The factors not stated, which would have scored marks, are the size of the charge on the ion and the magnetic field strength.

(i)   *A mass spectrometer has an inlet for ions which are separated, diverted and deflected before being pushed out again.*   0/5

(ii) *Speed, mass, number of electrons.*   2/3

(iii) *(84 × 0.0056) + (86 × 0.0990) + (87 × 0.0700) + (88 × 0.8254)*
      = 87.71 g   1/2

Although there is a correct final numerical value, with correct working, which would normally score 2 marks, the units of grams have been included, which is an error. Unit errors are penalized once only in a paper, and this is where the 1-mark penalty has been applied.

This answer achieved 5/10

A mark is lost because, although there is a reference to using electrons to bombard the sample, there is no mention of the formation of positive ions. There is also no mention of acceleration by an electric field, deflection in a magnetic field, or producing a current at the detector. Only the mention of vaporization scores.

Recognizing that the mass and charge on the ions affect the degree of deflection each scores a mark, but there is no mention of either the magnetic field strength or the speed of the ions.

A correct final answer is given, which also includes correct working. Each mass number has been multiplied by the percentage abundance and the total divided by 100.

(i) A mass spectrometer determines the mass of ions of elements. The mass spectrometer vaporizes the element and then bombards it with electrons. The element is an ion and is then deflected in one of the parts of the mass spectrometer. The mass spectrometer then determines how much the ion was deflected and then calculates the mass of the ion. 1/5

(ii) One factor that affects the degree of the deflection is the mass of the species that is being used in the mass spectrometer. Another factor is the degree of the ionization of the element and its charge. A third factor is the mass of the species being used by the mass spectrometer. 2/3

(iii) $\dfrac{(84 \times 0.56) + (86 \times 9.90) + (87 \times 7.00) + (88 \times 82.54)}{100}$

$= 87.71$ 2/2

This answer achieved 8/10

Marks are awarded for vaporizing the sample and for correct references to acceleration by an electric field and deflection in a magnetic field. Although bombardment by electrons is mentioned, the markscheme needed a reference to the ions being positive, which is missing. Also, although a detector is mentioned, there is no description of how the detector records the arrival of the ion (it generates an electric current), so the final mark is not awarded.

Three valid points are mentioned (mass and charge of the ions, and the magnetic field strength), so full marks are awarded.

A correct final answer, which also includes clear and detailed working, showing how the mass numbers and percentage abundances have been multiplied together.

(i) The element is first heated to vaporize it (unless it is a gas already). It is then bombarded with electrons, which knock an electron off the atoms. The ions are then accelerated by an electric field and then passed into a magnetic field, where they are deflected. They then hit the detector and are recorded on a computer. 3/5

(ii) The mass of the ion, what charge it has, and how strong the magnetic field is. 3/3

(iii)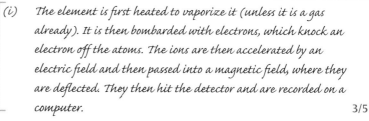

$\dfrac{(84 \times 0.56) + (86 \times 9.90) + (87 \times 7.00) + (88 \times 82.54)}{100}$

$= \dfrac{47.04 + 851.4 + 609 + 7263.52}{100}$

$= 87.71$ 2/2

The periodic table

You should know:

- elements are arranged in order of increasing atomic number

- the table is arranged in groups, which are vertical, and periods, which are horizontal.

You should be able to:

- relate the electron arrangement of an element to the position in the periodic table (for example, if an element is in period 3, it will have three shells of electrons)

- relate the number of electrons in the valence shell (outer shell) to the group number (for example, magnesium is in group 2, so it has two electrons in its outer shell).

Example

Nitrogen is found in period 2 and group 5 of the periodic table.

(a) Distinguish between the terms *period* and *group*.

A period refers to a horizontal row, and a group refers to a vertical column.

(b) State the electron arrangement of nitrogen and explain why it is found in period 2 and group 5 of the periodic table.

The electron arrangement of nitrogen is 2,5 (it has an atomic number of 7, so it has seven electrons). It is in period 2 because its electrons are in two energy levels. It is in group 5 because there are five electrons in the outer energy level.

Physical and chemical properties

You should know:

- atomic radii increase down a group, because new electron shells are added, and decrease across a period, because electrons are held more tightly by increasing nuclear charge

- the first ionization energy generally increases across a period and decreases down a group

- electronegativity is highest for fluorine and decreases down the table and to the left of fluorine, as atomic radii increase and attraction for the electrons is comparatively lower

- the ionic radii of cations (positive ions) are smaller than the corresponding atomic radii, because the remaining electrons are held more tightly

- the opposite is true for anions: the ionic radii of anions (negative ions) are larger than the corresponding atomic radii, because increased electron repulsion makes the radii larger

- the pH of the oxides of period 3 change from basic (groups 1 and 2), which are ionic, to acidic (groups 4–7), which are covalent.

You should be able to:

- compare the reactions of the alkali metals with water, for example

$$2Na(s) + 2H_2O(l) \rightarrow 2NaOH(aq) + H_2(g)$$

- compare the reactions of the alkali metals with halogens, for example

$$2Na(s) + Cl_2(g) \rightarrow 2NaCl(s)$$

Physical and chemical properties (continued)

- show how halogens react with halide solutions, for example

$$2NaBr(aq) + Cl_2(aq) \rightarrow 2NaCl(aq) + Br_2(aq)$$

- write equations for the reactions of Na_2O, MgO, P_4O_{10} and SO_2 with water.

Be prepared

- The data booklet contains information on all the periodic trends. It is therefore very important that you can explain the trends rather than just describe them.

- Non-metal oxides are responsible for acid rain, and you should know the source of these oxides.

Key definitions

- The first ionization energy is the energy needed to remove an electron from a gaseous atom or the energy needed to remove one mole of electrons from one mole of gaseous atoms, that is

$$X(g) \rightarrow X^+(g) + e^-$$

- Electronegativity is a measure of the ability of an atom to attract a shared pair of electrons towards itself.

Example

(a) Which statement about electronegativity is correct?

 A. Electronegativity decreases across a period.

 B. Electronegativity increases down a group.

 C. Metals generally have lower electronegativity values than non-metals.

 D. Noble gases have the highest electronegativity values.

Here the correct answer is C.

You should know that electronegativity increases across a period, decreases down a group and cannot be measured for the noble gases.

(b) Which of the following statements are correct?

 I. The melting points decrease from $Li \rightarrow Cs$ for the alkali metals.

 II. The melting points increase from $F \rightarrow I$ for the halogens.

 III. The melting points decrease from $Na \rightarrow Cl$ for the period 3 elements.

 A. I and II only

 B. I and III only

 C. II and III only

 D. I, II and III

The correct answer is A.

Here statement I is correct (so the answer cannot be C) and so is statement II (which means that the answer cannot be B). However, statement III is incorrect, as the melting points actually increase from Na to Si then decrease.

(c) Describe the acid–base character of the oxides of the period 3 elements Na to Ar. For sodium oxide and sulfur trioxide, write balanced equations to illustrate their acid–base character.

The oxides of Na and Mg are basic, and from Si to Cl they are acidic, and Ar has no oxide. The balanced equations are

$$Na_2O(s) + H_2O(l) \rightarrow 2NaOH(aq)$$
$$SO_2(g) + H_2O(l) \rightarrow H_2SO_3(aq)$$

Here states were not required for the mark, but you should include them if you know them. Also, you could mention that aluminium oxide behaves as both an acid and a base, and so is described as amphoteric.

(b) The graph of the first ionization energy plotted against atomic number for the first twenty elements shows periodicity.

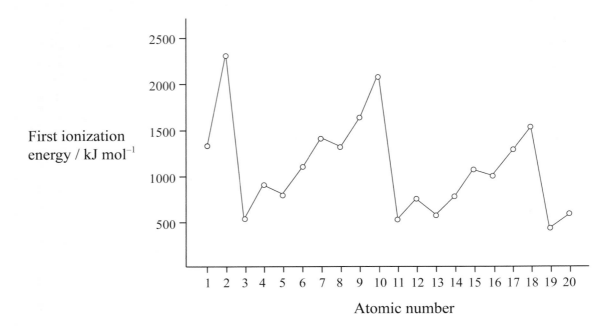

First ionization energy / kJ mol^{-1}

Atomic number

(i) Define the term *first ionization energy* and state what is meant by the term *periodicity*. [2]

(ii) State the electron arrangement of argon and explain why the noble gases, helium, neon and argon show the highest first ionization energies for their respective periods. [3]

(iii) A graph of atomic radius plotted against atomic number shows that the atomic radius decreases across a period. Explain why chlorine has a smaller atomic radius than sodium. [1]

(iv) Explain why a sulfide ion, S^{2-}, is larger than a chloride ion, Cl^-. [1]

(v) Explain why the melting points of the Group 1 metals (Li → Cs) decrease down the group whereas the melting points of the Group 7 elements (F → I) increase down the group. [3]

[Taken from paper 2, time zone 1, May 2009]

How do I approach the question?

(i) A precise definition of ionization energy is needed, remembering to include a reference to the atom being gaseous. Periodicity does not have a precise definition, and most students fail to make the point about properties repeating from one period to the next.

(ii) The electron arrangement needs to be written in full. Note that "electron arrangement" is the term used at standard level to refer to arrangements like 2,7, whereas "electron configuration" is the term used at higher level to refer to more detailed answers like $1s^2 2s^2 2p^5$. If you give a correct electron configuration in an answer at standard level, you will be awarded the mark. But you will not get the mark for giving an electron arrangement in an answer at higher level.

(iii) You should explain this in terms of the greater attraction because of greater nuclear charge.

(iv) You should refer to the numbers of protons and electrons and the attractions between them.

(v) You are asked to explain the trends in two different groups, so you have to understand the different types of bonding in these groups. A common error when referring to group 7 is not making clear whether the relevant type of bonding is covalent (between the atoms) or van der Waals (between the molecules).

What are the key areas of the syllabus?

- Key definitions and meanings
- Being able to write electron arrangements up to $Z = 20$
- Explaining trends across periods and down groups 1 and 7

This answer achieved 1/10

Neither mark is awarded because there is no mention of the need for the atom to be gaseous, and there is no reference to the idea that properties show a repeating pattern from one period to the next.

Marks are lost because there is no attempt to write the electron arrangement of argon, and there is no mention of the idea that noble gases have the greatest nuclear charge. Although there is a mention of bonds between the energy levels and the nucleus, there is no reference to electrons anywhere in the answer, and bonds should have been described as attractions.

The key idea that the nuclear charge in chlorine is greater than that in sodium is missing, so no mark is awarded.

The answer refers to the greater number of protons in the chloride ion and the stronger pull on the outer electrons, so the mark is awarded.

(i) First ionization energy means the energy required to pull off the first electron of the outermost energy level of an atom. Periodicity is the properties of groups/periods on the Periodic Table.
0/2

(ii) All of the energy levels of argon are filled, which means that the bonds between the energy levels and the nucleus is the strongest so the energy required to pull them apart would be high.
0/3

(iii) As more electrons are added across the period the pull on the energy level by the nucleus increases which pulls them closer decreasing the radius.
0/1

(iv) There are more protons in chloride ions pulling the same number of electrons as in the sulfide ion, so the pull is stronger – smaller radius.
1/1

(v) The bonds in Group 1 get weaker as they go down, but the bonds in Group 7 get stronger as they go down, so it's harder to break the bonds, increasing the melting point.
0/3

No marks are awarded because there is no indication of what particles are involved (atoms in group 1, molecules in group 7) and no mention of what the attractions between them are or why they change down each group.

This answer achieved 6/10

The first mark is lost because there is a reference to ability instead of energy and no mention of the need for the atom to be gaseous. The other mark is lost because there is no reference to the idea that properties show a repeating pattern.

Marks are awarded for the electron arrangement of argon and the mention of a full octet (or outer shell of electrons).

There is only 1 mark available for this part, and the student's answer is longer than it needs to be. However, the mark is awarded for the reference to the stronger attraction between the nucleus and the (outer) electron and the implication that the nuclear charge is greater in Cl than in Na.

No mark has been awarded because there is no mention of the nuclear charge or the attraction between the nucleus and the electrons in the outer energy level.

Full marks are awarded for stating that the number of energy levels increases, the mention of van der Waals' forces being responsible for the attractions, and for stating that these forces increase as the number of electrons increases.

(i) Ionisation energy is the ability of an element to remove an electron. Noble gases have the highest ionization energy. Periodicity is a general term given to all the different trends of a periodic table (examples – electronegativity, atomic radius, mp, bp)

0/2

(ii) $Ar = 1s^2 2s^2 2p^6 3s^2 3p^6$

Argon, a noble gas, has a full octet in the outermost energy level, so it is hard for any other element to remove an electron from this energy level.

2/3

(iii) Atomic radius is the distance between the electron of an outermost shell and the nucleus. Atomic radius increases as you go down a group as electrons are being added to a different energy level. However, as you go across a period, electrons are being added to the same energy level and simultaneously the proton is being added as well. Thus the nucleus will have a stronger attraction on the electron in the orbital as well. Thus, since Cl is farther across the period it has a smaller atomic radius than Na.

1/1

(iv) Cl^- and S^{2-} are both anions. S^{2-} is larger than Cl^- because it has 2 electrons added as opposed to chlorine's 1 electron. Thus more electrons will be further away from the nucleus.

0/1

(v) Group 1 (Li-Cs) are metals which mean that they have metallic bonding. As the number of energy levels increases the weaker the metallic bonding is therefore the melting point decrease as you decrease down group 1. However, group 7 has covalent - van der Waals' forces and these London forces becomes increasingly stronger if the number of electron orbitals increase thus melting points increase.

3/3

This answer achieved 8/10

The definition of first ionization energy is correct, and the description of how electronegativity varies in the periodic table clearly gets across the idea of a repeating pattern.

Marks are awarded for the electron arrangement of argon and the full outer energy level.

Although this answer is brief, it answers the question perfectly, so the mark is awarded.

The answer clearly identifies the reason for the difference in radius, so the mark is awarded.

Although this answer is a good one, a mark is lost for stating that, for the group 7 elements, the bonds get stronger as the masses increase down the group. Here "bonds" might mean covalent bonds, which would be wrong—it is the intermolecular (van der Waals') forces that get stronger.

(i) First ionization energy is the energy needed to remove an electron from the outer shell of a gaseous atom.

Periodicity is when a property like electronegativity is similar for all the elements in a group. So lithium has a low value, and this increases across the period, but when starting the next period with sodium it is low again. **2/2**

(ii) Ar has its electrons arranged as 2.8.8, so the outer shell is full and stable, so it is hard for an electron to be removed. **2/3**

(iii) Chlorine has more protons in its nucleus than sodium, so it attracts the outer electrons more strongly, pulling them closer to the nucleus. **1/1**

(iv) Cl^- has 1 more proton than S^{2-} but the same number of electrons in the same shells. So the electrons are less strongly attracted in S^{2-} so it is larger. **1/1**

(v) The Group 1 metals get bigger down the group, so the delocalized electrons have a weaker hold on the metal ions, so the melting points go down. The Group 7 elements have bigger atomic masses down the group, so the bonds are stronger and need more energy to break. **2/3**

8. Bonding

Ionic bonding

You should know:

- ionic bonds form by electron transfer between elements of differing electronegativity, so between metals and non-metals
- ionic bonding is due to the electrostatic attraction of oppositely charged ions
- ionic bonding leads to the formation of a regular framework of alternating positive and negative ions described as a lattice.

You should be able to:

- deduce the formula of ionic compounds by knowing the details in the table.

Group number	Electrons lost	Charge on ion	Group number	Electrons gained	Charge on ion
1	1	1^+	5	3	3^-
2	2	2^+	6	2	2^-
3	3	3^+	7	1	1^-

Be prepared

- You should know and be able to use the formulas for carbonate (CO_3^{2-}), nitrate (NO_3^-), sulfate (SO_4^{2-}), hydroxide (OH^-), phosphate (PO_4^{3-}), hydrogencarbonate (HCO_3^-) and ammonium (NH_4^+).

Example

What is the formula for the compound formed by calcium and nitrogen?

A. CaN

B. Ca_2N

C. Ca_2N_3

D. Ca_3N_2

Correct answer is D.

Since calcium is in group 2 it is 2^+, and nitrogen is in group 5 so it is 3^-. You then need to "swap and drop" to balance the charges, so the correct answer is D.

Covalent bonding

You should know:

- covalent bonds form when electrons are shared between nuclei

- single bonds are longer and weaker than double bonds, and triple bonds are shorter and stronger than double bonds, so C—C is more easily broken than C=C, which is more easily broken than C≡C

- dative covalent (coordinate) bonds form when both the electrons being shared have come from the same atom

- the structure and bonding in the allotropes of carbon and in silicon and silicon dioxide, as in the table below.

You should be able to:

- deduce the Lewis (electron dot or dot–cross) structures of simple molecules

- use valence shell electron pair repulsion (VSEPR) theory to predict the bond angle and shape around an atom in a molecule or ion

- predict whether a bond will be polar by looking at the electronegativities of the atoms (the bigger the difference, the more polar the bond)

- predict whether a molecule is polar by looking at the bond polarity and shape of the molecule—in a polar molecule, the dipoles do not cancel out (they are not symmetrical).

Be prepared

- In Lewis structures, a pair of electrons can be represented by two dots (● ●) or two crosses (✗✗) or a line (—).

- Make sure that you include all the valence electrons of all the atoms.

Example

(a) Draw the Lewis structure of methanoic acid, HCOOH.

$$H-C\begin{array}{c}\ddot{O}\\ \ddot{O}-H\end{array}$$

Here dots and lines are shown, but dots and crosses would also be fine.

(b) In methanoic acid, predict the bond angle around the
   (i) carbon atom.
   (ii) oxygen atom bonded to the hydrogen atom.

   (i) O—C—O = 120°
   This is because using VSEPR theory there are three negative charge centres repelling equally, leading to a bond angle of 120°.

   (ii) C—O—H = 105°
   (Any value between 100° and 109° would get a mark.)
   There are four negative charge centres leading to a bond angle of 109.5°, but the lone pairs on the oxygen cause greater repulsion than the bonding pairs, so the angle is less.

(c) State and explain the relationship between the length and strength of the bonds between the carbon atom and the two oxygen atoms in methanoic acid.

   length: C=O < C—O, so C—O is longer than C=O
   strength: C=O > C—O, so C=O is stronger than C—O
   This is because the greater number of electrons between the nuclei in a double bond (four instead of two in a single bond) pull the atoms together, so the bond is shorter for a double bond. Also, because of this, the double bonds require greater energy to break.

	Diamond (C)	Graphite (C)	Fullerene (C₆₀)	Silicon (Si)	Silicon dioxide (SiO₂)
Structure	giant: all C atoms bonded to 4 others	giant: all C atoms bonded to 3 others in a layer	simple: all C atoms bonded to 3 others in a ball	giant: all Si atoms bonded to 4 others	giant: all Si atoms bonded to 4 oxygens, each oxygen bonded to 2 silicons
Bonding	covalent	covalent	covalent	covalent	covalent
Shape and bond angles	carbons arranged tetrahedrally, bond angle 109.5°	carbons in trigonal planar arrangement, bond angle 120°	carbons in trigonal planar arrangement, bond angle 120°	silicons arranged tetrahedrally, bond angle 109.5°	silicons arranged tetrahedrally, bond angle 109.5°

Metallic bonding

You should know:

- metallic bonds are formed by the electrostatic attraction of delocalized electrons for the lattice of positive metallic ions.

You should be able to:

- explain that metals conduct electricity because of their delocalized electrons

- explain that metals are malleable because there are no directional bonds to be broken—the ions can slide over each other when a force is applied.

Be prepared

- You should appreciate the economic importance of iron and other metals.

Intermolecular forces

You should know:

- intermolecular forces hold molecules together and are much weaker than covalent bonds

- strength of hydrogen bonds > dipole–dipole > temporary dipole/van der Waals' forces.

You should be able to:

- deduce the intermolecular force present between molecules from looking at the structure of the molecules

- predict relative boiling points.

Be prepared

- Hydrogen bonding can only occur when hydrogen is **directly** attached to F, O or N.

Example

(a) List the following substances in order of increasing boiling point (lowest first).

$$CH_3CHO \qquad C_2H_6 \qquad CH_3COOH \qquad C_2H_5OH$$

The answer is $C_2H_6 < CH_3CHO < C_2H_5OH < CH_3COOH$.

C_2H_6 only has van der Waals' forces, and because boiling point depends on intermolecular forces and least energy is required to break van der Waals' forces, this has the lowest boiling point. C_2H_5OH and CH_3COOH both can hydrogen bond, and because this is a stronger intermolecular force, more energy is needed to break the bonds, so their boiling points are higher. However, CH_3COOH is a heavier molecule, so van der Waals' forces are greater. As well as this, the hydrogen bonding is stronger, as there is greater polarity. In CH_3CHO there are dipole–dipole forces, which are weaker than hydrogen bonds but stronger than van der Waals' forces.

(b) State whether each compound in part (a) is polar or non-polar.

The answer is C_2H_6 is non-polar, and CH_3CHO, C_2H_5OH and CH_3COOH are polar.

This is because in C_2H_6 the electronegativities of C and H are similar so no dipole arises. In the other molecules a dipole is produced between the O and C, and between the O and H, as the electronegativity of O is higher. Also the molecules are not symmetrical, so the dipoles do not cancel out.

Physical properties

You should know:

- that physical properties depend on bonding and structure, as shown in the table.

Property	Structure			
	Ionic	Simple molecular	Giant molecular	Metallic
Melting and boiling points	high	low	high	high
Volatility	low	high	low	low
Electrical conductivity	good as liquid, poor as solid	poor	poor (except graphite)	good
Solubility in polar solvent	good	poor	poor	poor
Solubility in non-polar solvent	poor	good	poor	poor

Example

The diagrams below represent the structures of iodine, sodium and sodium iodide.

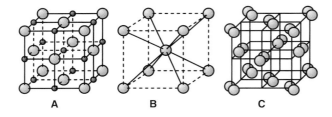

A   B   C

(a) Identify which of the structures (**A**, **B** and **C**) correspond to iodine, sodium and sodium iodide.

A = sodium iodide, B = sodium and C = iodine

We know this because sodium iodide as a compound must have different atoms, and these are arranged in a lattice of alternating ions, so it is A. Iodine is a diatomic element, so has to be C. So sodium is B.

(b) State the type of bonding in each structure.

The bonding is A = ionic, B = metallic, and C = covalent between atoms and van der Waals' forces between molecules.

A contains a metal and non-metal, so electron transfer takes place to form ions. In B metal atoms share their valence electrons to form a sea of delocalized electrons. In C diatomic molecules are held in place by van der Waals' forces.

(c) Sodium and sodium iodide can both conduct electricity when molten, but only sodium can conduct electricity when solid. Explain this difference in conductivity in terms of the structures of sodium and sodium iodide.

Conduction of electricity requires that either electrons or ions can flow. In sodium, there are delocalized electrons that can flow around the positive metal ions when sodium is solid or liquid. In sodium iodide, the oppositely charged ions are held in place by ionic bonds, and as a solid this prevents the ions moving. When molten, the ions are able to move to the oppositely charged electrodes where they gain or lose electrons.

(d) Explain the high volatility of iodine compared to sodium and sodium iodide.

Volatility refers to the tendency of a substance to vaporize, so high volatility means a low boiling point and vice versa. So the answer is that in iodine only the weak intermolecular forces need to be broken, but in sodium iodide it is necessary to break the strong ionic bonds, which requires far more energy.

6. (a) (i) Draw the Lewis structures for carbon monoxide, CO, carbon dioxide, CO_2 and methanol, CH_3OH. [3]

(ii) List, with an explanation, the three compounds in order of increasing carbon to oxygen bond length (shortest first). [2]

(b) Predict the shape and bond angles for the following species:

(i) CO_2 [2]

(ii) CO_3^{2-} [2]

(iii) BF_4^- [2]

[Taken from paper 2, time zone 1, May 2009]

How do I approach the question?

(a) In part (i), for each atom, you need to consider which group of the periodic table the element is in, and so decide how many electron pairs surround it. Then show each atom separately, with all bonding pairs shown. Then decide how many non-bonding pairs there are and include them. Note that you can use any of the three ways shown in the syllabus to represent the non-bonding pairs. When a molecule or ion has three or more atoms, you can draw its shape, but this is not necessary if the question asks only for a Lewis structure. In (ii), you have to remember the link between number of bonds and bond length.

(b) You need to be able to apply the VSEPR theory to predict shapes and bond angles. This means working out how many electron pairs there are around the central atom. This tells you the overall shape of the electron distribution. Then you have to decide how many are bonding pairs and how many are non-bonding pairs. This tells you the shape made by the atoms and also whether you have to adjust the bond angle to take into account the fact that non-bonding pairs repel more than bonding pairs.

What are the key areas of the syllabus?

- Being able to draw Lewis structures
- Being able to explain the link between bond length and the number of bonds between atoms
- Using the VSEPR theory to predict shapes and bond angles

This answer achieved 4/11

Although the methanol structure is correct, carbon monoxide has a double bond instead of a triple bond, and there should not be any non-bonding pairs of electrons on the central atom in carbon dioxide.

Although the order is correct, the answer to the previous part did not have any triple bonds, so the mark for explanation, which needed a reference to triple bonds, has not been awarded.

The shape and bond angle are both correct, based on the electrons in two double bonds around the carbon atom repelling each other.

The shape and bond angle are wrong.

(a) (i)

$\overset{x}{\underset{x}{C}} = \overset{..}{\underset{..}{O}}$ $\overset{..}{\underset{..}{O}} = \overset{x}{\underset{x}{C}} = \overset{..}{\underset{..}{O}}$ $H \overset{x}{\underset{H}{\overset{H}{C}}} \overset{x}{O} H$ **1/3**

(ii) Double bonds are shorter than single bonds so the order is carbon monoxide, carbon dioxide and methanol.   **1/2**

(b) (i) CO_2 is linear with a bond angle of 180°.   **2/2**

(ii) CO_3^{-2} is a pyramid with a bond angle of 100°.   **0/2**

(iii) BF_4^- is square planar with a bond angle of 90°.   **0/2**

The shape and bond angle are wrong.

This answer achieved 6/11

The structures for carbon monoxide and carbon dioxide are correct, although there is a non-bonding pair missing on methanol. Note that lines as well as pairs of dots or crosses can be used to represent non-bonding electron pairs.

The order is correct and has been justified by referring to the numbers of bonds.

The shape and bond angle are both correct.

(a) (i)

$|C \equiv O|$ $\overline{O} = C = \overline{O}$ $H - \overset{H}{\underset{H}{\overset{|}{C}}} - \overline{O} - H$ **2/3**

(ii) The more bonds there are between atoms the closer the atoms are held together and the bond is shorter. The order is carbon monoxide, then carbon dioxide then methanol.   **2/2**

(b) (i) CO_2 is linear with a bond angle of 180°.   **2/2**

(ii) CO_3^{2-} is a pyramid with a bond angle of 90°.   **0/2**

(iii) BF_4^- is also a pyramid but with bond angles of 120°.   **0/2**

This answer achieved 11/11

All three structures are correct.

A correct order has been given, justified by reference to the numbers of bonds involved.

The shape and bond angle are both correct, based on the electrons in two double bonds around the carbon atom repelling each other equally.

The shape and bond angle are both correct, based on the electrons in three bonds around the carbon atom repelling each other equally.

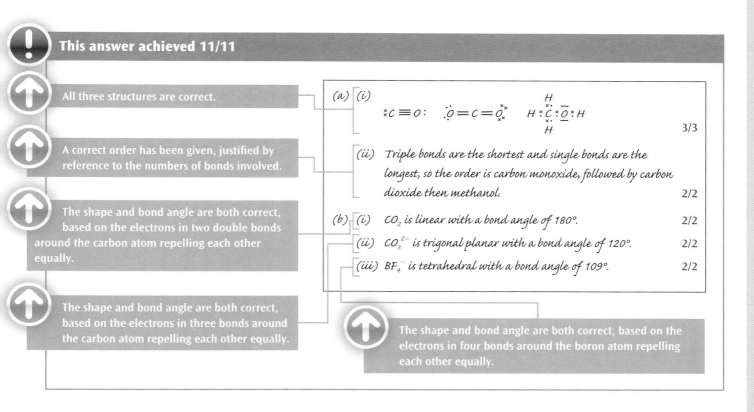

(a) (i)

3/3

(ii) Triple bonds are the shortest and single bonds are the longest, so the order is carbon monoxide, followed by carbon dioxide then methanol.

2/2

(b) (i) CO_2 is linear with a bond angle of 180°.

2/2

(ii) CO_3^{2-} is trigonal planar with a bond angle of 120°.

2/2

(iii) BF_4^- is tetrahedral with a bond angle of 109°.

2/2

The shape and bond angle are both correct, based on the electrons in four bonds around the boron atom repelling each other equally.

(iii)   Describe the structure and bonding in silicon dioxide and carbon dioxide.   *[4]*

[Taken from paper 2, time zone 1, May 2009]

How do I approach the question?

The question refers to both structure and bonding, so your answer should mention both points for both compounds.

Although the question does not mention drawing a diagram, you should consider whether a diagram would help—sometimes a well-labelled diagram can score full marks.

The 4-mark allocation suggests 1 mark each for of the structure and bonding in each compound.

What are the key areas of the syllabus?

- The types of bonding in the substances covered in the syllabus
- How structure depends on the type of bonding

This answer achieved 1/4

Although silicon dioxide can be described as a giant molecule, "big" does not have quite the same meaning. In any case, using "ionic" and "molecule" to describe the same substance is a contradiction. In questions about bonding, such contradictions are always penalized. For carbon dioxide, "covalent" is correct, but "small" does not have the same meaning as "individual" or "discrete".

> Silicon dioxide is a big ionic molecule and carbon dioxide is a small covalent molecule.
>
> 1/4

This answer achieved 2/4

Although silicon dioxide is correctly described as a giant molecule, the type of bonding has not been mentioned. The type of bonding in carbon dioxide is correct, but there is no indication of whether its structure is that of an individual molecule made up of just three atoms or of a macromolecular structure.

> Silicon dioxide is a giant molecule with each silicon atom joined to 4 oxygen atoms. In carbon dioxide each carbon atom is joined to 2 oxygen atoms by covalent bonds.
>
> 2/4

This answer achieved 4/4

The words used in the answer are enough to score full marks—the types of structure and bonding have been stated for both compounds. The diagrams are correct and will have taken little time to draw. Although diagrams were not required by the question, it is a good idea to draw them, because sometimes a missing vital word can score from the diagram. For example, if "individual" had been missed out of the description of carbon dioxide, then the mark could have been awarded from the diagram.

> Silicon dioxide is a macromolecule made of lots of silicon and oxygen atoms joined together by covalent bonds in a structure like this
>
> $$\begin{array}{c} O \\ | \\ O - Si - O \\ | \\ O \end{array}$$
>
> Carbon dioxide exists as individual molecules containing carbon and oxygen atoms joined by covalent bonds as follows
>
> $O = C = O$
>
> 4/4

(b) The graph below shows the boiling points of hybrides of group 5. Discuss the variation in the boiling points. *[4]*

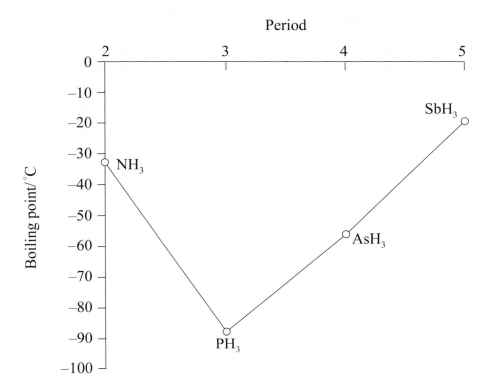

(c) Explain, using diagrams, why CO and NO_2 are polar molecules but CO_2 is a non-polar molecule. *[5]*

[Taken from paper 2, time zone 2, May 2009]

How do I approach the question?

(b) The command term **discuss** means that you should consider **all** the relevant points and write them in a logical order. Although there are only four points on the graph, can you recognize the general trend and any exception? Boiling points of simple molecular substances indicate the strength of forces between the molecules. You need to consider what types of intermolecular force are involved here, and why the same type of intermolecular force is stronger in some substances.

(c) You must draw a diagram for each of the three molecules mentioned, and write an explanation of why two are polar and one is not. A common error in this type of question is to confuse the polarity of a bond with the polarity of a molecule—these ideas are connected but are not the same.

What are the key areas of the syllabus?

- Working out bond polarities from electronegativity values
- Working out shapes of molecules using the VSEPR theory
- Understanding the difference between a polar bond and a polar molecule

This answer achieved 2/9

The first sentence is just a description of the trend that shows no chemical understanding, and the second is too vague to be worth any marks.

(b) The boiling point goes down once, then up twice. This is to do with the size of the molecules. 0/4

(c) CO is polar because O is more electronegative than C

C=O

The answer for CO does not score because a correct statement about electronegativity difference has not gone any further—there is no reference to charge separation or dipole formation. The answer for NO_2 also fails to score for the same reason and because the diagram does not show the bent nature of the molecule. However, the shape of CO_2 is correct, and the statement about polarities cancelling is a correct way of explaining the lack of polarity.

NO_2 is polar because O is more electronegative than N

O=N=O

CO_2 is non-polar because although O is more electronegative than C the polarities cancel out because the molecule is linear.

O=C=O 2/5

This answer achieved 4/9

The statement about the increase scores for the reference to the period numbers and the molecular size, although neither of the forces is identified.

(b) The boiling points increase from period 3 to 5 as the atoms and molecules get bigger, so the forces needed to separate them get bigger. 2/4

(c) CO and NO_2 are polar because they have polar bonds that do not cancel out but CO_2 has polar bonds that cancel out.

The diagrams are all linear and unlabelled, and the only correct one is for CO_2. The point about polar bonds cancelling out in CO_2 is just about good enough to score.

C—O

O=N=O

O=C=O 2/5

This answer achieved 9/9

This answer covers all the points in the markscheme—the correct trend, the trend in the strength of the van der Waals' forces, and the greater strength of hydrogen bonding.

This is an excellent answer that explains the difference between polar bonds and polar molecules and shows correctly labelled diagrams.

(b) The general trend in boiling point is shown from PH_3 to SbH_3 – as the molecules get bigger the van der Waals' forces between them get stronger so more energy is needed to separate them. NH_3 is different because it has hydrogen bonding, which is a much stronger force than van der Waals, so needs more energy to boil.

4/4

(c) In all three molecules oxygen is more electronegative than the other atoms, so all the bonds are polar.

In CO, the molecule is polar:

$$\overset{\delta+}{C} = \overset{\delta-}{O}$$

NO_2 is polar because the molecule is V-shaped and the nitrogen is the positive end and the oxygens the negative end:

$$\overset{\delta+}{N}$$
$$O \qquad O$$
$$\delta- \qquad \delta-$$

CO_2 is not polar because the molecule is linear and the two bond polarities cancel:

$$\overset{\longleftrightarrow}{O} = C = \overset{\longleftrightarrow}{O}$$

5/5

9. Energetics

Exothermic and endothermic reactions and bond enthalpies

You should know:

- that combustion (burning in oxygen) and neutralization are exothermic processes

- ΔH (the enthalpy change) is negative for exothermic reactions and ΔH is positive for endothermic reactions.

You should be able to:

- recognize an exothermic reaction as one that raises temperature

- recognize an endothermic reaction as one that leads to a decrease in temperature

- use enthalpy level diagrams

- understand that in an exothermic reaction the products are of lower energy than the reactants

- understand that in an endothermic reaction the reactants are of lower energy than the products

- explain that bond breaking uses energy (is endothermic) and bond making releases energy (is exothermic)

- appreciate that it is the balance between bond breaking and bond making that determines whether a reaction will be exothermic or endothermic.

Be prepared

- Standard conditions in thermodynamics are a temperature of 298 K (25°C), a pressure of 101.3 kPa (1 atmosphere), and 1 molar concentration of solutions.

Key definitions

- In an exothermic reaction, energy is released to the surroundings.

- In an endothermic reaction, energy is absorbed from the surroundings.

- Standard enthalpy change of reaction is the heat energy transferred when molar amounts of substances in a balanced equation react under standard thermodynamic conditions.

- Average bond enthalpy is the energy (in kJ) needed to break one mole of a particular covalent bond in the gaseous state into gaseous atoms. It is an average because it is averaged over all the environments that the bond is found in.

Example

Which statements are correct for an endothermic reaction?

    I.   The system absorbs heat.
    II. The enthalpy change is positive.
    III. The bond enthalpy total for the reactants is greater than for the products.

A. I and II only

B. I and III only

C. II and III only

D. I, II and III

Correct answer is D.

Statement I is correct, as the system absorbs heat, which decreases the temperature (so C cannot be the correct answer). Statement II is also correct, because the enthalpy change is positive (so B is not the correct answer). Statement III is also correct, as bond breaking absorbs more heat than bond breaking releases in this case. So all three statements are correct, and the correct answer is D.

Calculation of enthalpy changes and Hess's law

You should know:

- the equation $\Delta H = m \times c \times \Delta T$, and use it to calculate enthalpy changes
- in experiments measuring enthalpy changes, the greatest error is always heat loss.

You should be able to:

- design experiments to measure the enthalpy change of combustion using the energy evolved to heat a known mass of water
- design experiments to measure the enthalpy change in aqueous solution
- calculate both empirical and molecular formulas from given data
- work out the enthalpy change in a reaction using known enthalpy changes of two or three reactions with enthalpy cycles or by rearranging equations.

Be prepared

- The specific heat capacity (c) of a substance is the amount of energy needed to raise the temperature of 1 g of it by 1°C. The specific heat capacity of water and aqueous solutions is $4.18\,J\,g^{-1}\,K^{-1}$.

Example

(a) Consider the specific heat capacity of the following metals.

Metal	Specific heat capacity / $J\,kg^{-1}\,K^{-1}$
Cu	385
Ag	234
Au	130
Pt	134

Which metal will show the greatest temperature increase if 50 J of heat is supplied to a 0.001 kg sample of each metal at the same initial temperature?

    A. Cu
    B. Ag
    C. Au
    D. Pt

Answer C.

The specific heat capacity (c) is how much energy is needed to raise the temperature of 1 g of substance by 1°C, so a low c means that less energy is needed to raise the temperature, so in this case the answer is C.

(b) The mass m (in g) of a substance of specific heat capacity c (in $J\,g^{-1}\,K^{-1}$) increases by t°C. What is the heat change in J?

    A. mct
    B. $mc(t + 273)$
    C. $\dfrac{mct}{1000}$
    D. $\dfrac{mc(t + 273)}{1000}$

A is the correct answer.

Heat change is equal to m × c × t, and since we want the answer in J, this makes A the correct answer. Answer C would be correct if you needed the answer in kJ. Answers B and D are clever distracters, because temperature is in kelvins. But there is no need to add 273 because it is a temperature change and this is the same in degrees Celsius and kelvins.

(c) Using the equations below:

$$C(s) + O_2(g) \rightarrow CO_2(g) \qquad \Delta H = -390\,kJ$$
$$Mn(s) + O_2(g) \rightarrow MnO_2(s) \qquad \Delta H = -520\,kJ$$

what is ΔH (in kJ) for the following reaction?

$$MnO_2(s) + C(s) \rightarrow Mn(s) + CO_2(g)$$

    A. 910
    B. 130
    C. −130
    D. −910

The correct answer is B.

To answer the question, you need to rearrange the equations given so that when you combine them you get:

$$MnO_2(s) + C(s) \rightarrow Mn(s) + CO_2(g)$$

So the second equation in the question needs to be reversed and added to the first:

$$MnO_2(s) \rightarrow Mn(s) + O_2(g) \qquad \Delta H = +520\,kJ$$
$$C(s) + O_2(g) \rightarrow CO_2(g) \qquad \Delta H = -390\,kJ$$

The oxygen molecules appear on both sides of the equation when we combine these two equations and so they cancel out, leaving us with the equation we need:

$$MnO_2(s) + C(s) \rightarrow Mn(s) + CO_2(g) \quad \Delta H = ?$$

Adding the values (+520) + (−390) gives us ΔH = 130 kJ. So the correct answer is B.

2. Two students were asked to use information from the Data Booklet to calculate a value for the enthalpy of hydrogenation of ethene to form ethane.

$$C_2H_4(g) + H_2(g) \rightarrow C_2H_6(g)$$

John used the average bond enthalpies from Table 10. Marit used the values of enthalpies of combustion from Table 12.

(a) Calculate the value for the enthalpy of hydrogenation of ethene obtained using the average bond enthalpies given in Table 10.

[2]

(b) Marit arranged the values she found in Table 12 into an energy cycle.

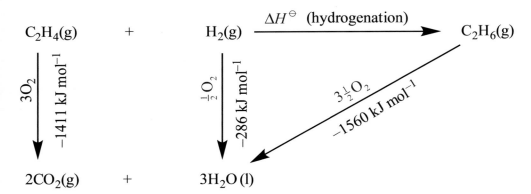

Calculate the value for the enthalpy of hydrogenation of ethene from the energy cycle. [1]

(c) Suggest **one** reason why John's answer is slightly less accurate than Marit's answer. [1]

(d) John then decided to determine the enthalpy of hydrogenation of cyclohexene to produce cyclohexane.

$$C_6H_{10}(l) + H_2(g) \rightarrow C_6H_{12}(l)$$

(i) Use the average bond enthalpies to deduce a value for the enthalpy of hydrogenation of cyclohexene.

[1]

(ii) The percentage difference between these two methods (average bond enthalpies and enthalpies of combustion) is greater for cyclohexene than it was for ethene. John's hypothesis was that it would be the same. Determine why the use of average bond enthalpies is less accurate for the cyclohexene equation shown above, than it was for ethene. Deduce what extra information is needed to provide a more accurate answer.

[2]

[Taken from paper 2, time zone 1, May 2009]

How do I approach the question?

(a) You need to choose the right bond enthalpy values from the data booklet, remembering that C—C and C=C are different. Check that you have worked out the right number of each value to use. It is a good idea to write the structures out, so you are less likely to make a mistake. It is also a good idea to make separate lists of the bonds broken and formed, so you can easily add them up. Finally, remember that it is the sum for the bonds broken minus the sum for the bonds made, and to include the sign, whether + or −.

(b) You are applying Hess's law. If you are familiar with the energy cycle in the way it is drawn in the question, then this should be straightforward. If you do not recognize this layout, you can still use the values on the arrows in the method you are more familiar with.

(c) You need to realize the significance of **average** values used in (a), compared to the **actual** values used here.

(d) In part (i), you could do a calculation like the one in (a), but the question uses **deduce**, not **calculate**. Try comparing this equation with the one in (a) and figure out why you do not need to do a calculation. Part (ii) is a tough one—a difficult point and a lot of words to read. Think about the exact definition of average bond enthalpy and about states of matter.

What are the key areas of the syllabus?

- Calculation of enthalpy changes for reactions from average bond enthalpy values
- Applying Hess's law to an energy cycle
- Comparing values obtained from the above methods

This answer achieved 1/7

There are a number of mistakes in this answer, so no marks are awarded. The number of C—H bonds broken should be four, not two, the subtraction to get the enthalpy change has been done the wrong way round, and the value found in the first line has been misread.

The signs are wrong, so the mark cannot be awarded.

There is nothing relevant in this answer—the student has not mentioned the difference between average and specific values.

Although this is not the correct answer, the student has deduced correctly that the answer is the same as that in part (a), so the mark is awarded.

(a) Bonds broken need 612 + (2 × 413) + 436 = 1874 kJ
Bonds formed are 347 + (6 × 413) = 2825 kJ
The enthalpy change is 2825 − 1872 = 953 kJ   0/2

(b) 1411 + 286 − 1560 = 137   0/1

(c) Because John's answer is merely taking the enthalpies of the bonds and reversing them to break them, whereas Marit's is taking the enthalpy of combustion energy to break the bonds more directly.   0/1

(d) (i) This reaction is the same as the one in part (a) so the answer is the same 953 kJ   1/1

(ii) Because cyclohexene has a greater molar mass than ethane. The enthalpy of combustion of cyclohexene is needed to provide a more accurate answer.   0/2

There is nothing relevant in this answer—the key idea of change of state is missing.

This answer achieved 3/7

A correct method has been used and the calculations have been done correctly, but the breaking of the H—H bond has been left out. This means that 1 mark can be awarded for the final subtraction.

A correct value is given, with sign and units.

There is nothing relevant in this answer—the student has not mentioned the difference between average and specific values.

Although this is not the correct answer according to the markscheme, it is the same as that in part (a), which is what it should be.

There is nothing relevant in this answer—the key idea of change of state is missing.

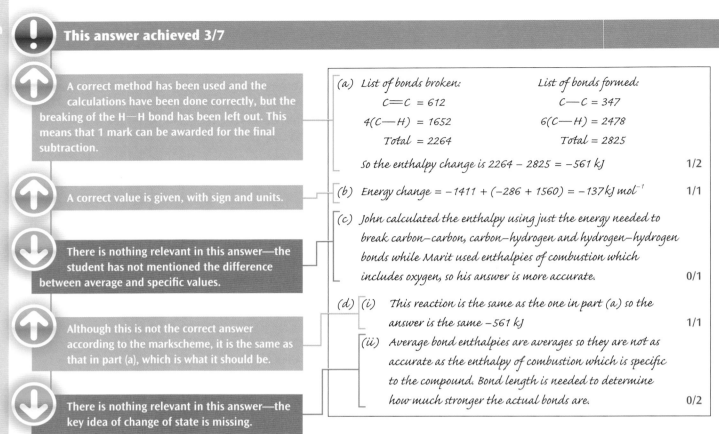

(a) List of bonds broken:

    $C=C = 612$

    $4(C—H) = 1652$

    Total = 2264

List of bonds formed:

    $C—C = 347$

    $6(C—H) = 2478$

    Total = 2825

So the enthalpy change is 2264 − 2825 = −561 kJ   1/2

(b) Energy change = − 1411 + (−286 + 1560) = −137 kJ mol⁻¹   1/1

(c) John calculated the enthalpy using just the energy needed to break carbon–carbon, carbon–hydrogen and hydrogen–hydrogen bonds while Marit used enthalpies of combustion which includes oxygen, so his answer is more accurate.   0/1

(d) (i) This reaction is the same as the one in part (a) so the answer is the same −561 kJ   1/1

    (ii) Average bond enthalpies are averages so they are not as accurate as the enthalpy of combustion which is specific to the compound. Bond length is needed to determine how much stronger the actual bonds are.   0/2

This answer achieved 5/7

A correct method has been used and the calculations are clearly set out. The right values have been used from the data booklet and the need to multiply the C—H value by 2 because two bonds are formed has not been overlooked.

(a) The energies given out when bonds are broken are

C═C = 612

H—H = 436

Total = 1048

The energies given out when the new bonds are formed

C—C = 347

2(C—H) = 826

Total = 1173

So the enthalpy change is $-125\,kJ\,mol^{-1}$ 2/2

Although no words are used, this is a correct method and great care has been taken with the + and − signs.

(b) $-1411 + [(-286 + 1560) = 1274] = -137\,kJ\,mol^{-1}$ 1/1

The explanation is good enough to score the mark—although "average" is missing, the idea of actual values being used by Marit is included.

(c) Bond energies vary between different compounds but Marit used the actual values for the reaction.   1/1

(d) (i) The same bonds are broken and formed in this reaction as in the ethene reaction, so the answer is the same
$-125\,kJ\,mol^{-1}$ 1/1

A correct answer ($-125\,kJ\,mol^{-1}$) is given, and also justified with a reason.

(ii) Cyclohexene has a ring structure so its bonding is different from ethene's. The extra information needed is the stability of the ring.   0/2

There is nothing relevant in this answer. Very few students compared the state symbols in the two equations given in the question and realized that the (l) symbols in part (d) were important. The energy required to convert liquid to gas, or the energy released when a gas becomes a liquid, needs to be taken into account.

---

6. In some countries, ethanol is mixed with gasoline (petrol) to produce a fuel for cars called gasohol.

(a) (i) Define the term *average bond enthalpy*.   [2]

(ii) Use the information from Table 10 of the Data Booklet to determine the standard enthalpy change for the complete combustion of ethanol.

$$CH_3CH_2OH(g) + 3O_2(g) \rightarrow 2CO_2(g) + 3H_2O(g)$$ [3]

(iii) The standard enthalpy change for the complete combustion of octane, C_8H_{18}, is $-5471\,kJ\,mol^{-1}$. Calculate the amount of energy produced in kJ when 1 g of ethanol and 1 g of octane is burned completely in air.   [2]

[Taken from paper 2, time zone 2, May 2009]

How do I approach the question?

(i) You simply have to remember an exact definition that includes the key ideas.

(ii) You need to choose the right bond enthalpy values from the data booklet, remembering that C—O and C=O are different. Check that you have worked out the right number of each value to use. It is a good idea to write the structures out, so you are less likely to make a mistake. It is also a good idea to make separate lists of the bonds broken and formed, so you can easily add them up. Finally, remember that it is the sum for the bonds broken minus the sum for the bonds made, and to include the sign, whether + or −.

(iii) You are given the amount of heat produced by burning 1 mol of octane. Using the relative formula mass of octane, you can work out what amount of heat would come from burning 1000 g of octane. The answer for ethanol is worked out similarly, except that you have to use your answer to (ii).

What are the key areas of the syllabus?

- The definition of average bond enthalpy
- Calculation of enthalpy changes for reactions from average bond enthalpy values
- Applying simple proportion in converting enthalpy change values from kJ mol^{-1} to kJ kg^{-1}

This answer achieved 3/7

The essential term "gaseous" has been left out, and there is no attempt to explain the meaning of average.

Although a correct method has been used, one of the bonds broken is wrong: for O$_2$ the value for O—O has been used instead of that for O=O. There is also a mistake in the bonds formed: in 3H$_2$O there are six H—O bonds, not three. However, a mark has been awarded for the correct subtraction of two wrong totals.

The correct methods have been used and the value for octane is correct. Although the answer for ethanol is incorrect, this is because the value from the previous part has been used. This is a case where the error carried forward principle leads to full marks.

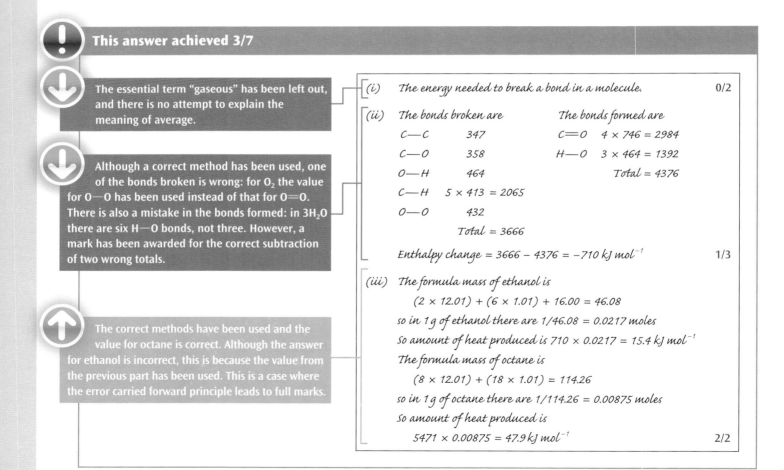

(i) The energy needed to break a bond in a molecule.   0/2

(ii) The bonds broken are   The bonds formed are

    C—C   347   C=O   4 × 746 = 2984

    C—O   358   H—O   3 × 464 = 1392

    O—H   464   Total = 4376

    C—H 5 × 413 = 2065

    O—O   432

         Total = 3666

Enthalpy change = 3666 − 4376 = −710 kJ mol^{-1} 1/3

(iii) The formula mass of ethanol is

    (2 × 12.01) + (6 × 1.01) + 16.00 = 46.08

so in 1 g of ethanol there are 1/46.08 = 0.0217 moles

So amount of heat produced is 710 × 0.0217 = 15.4 kJ mol^{-1}

The formula mass of octane is

    (8 × 12.01) + (18 × 1.01) = 114.26

so in 1 g of octane there are 1/114.26 = 0.00875 moles

So amount of heat produced is

    5471 × 0.00875 = 47.9 kJ mol^{-1} 2/2

This answer achieved 4/7

This is a correct definition—all the key points are included.

(i) This is the energy needed to break a bond in a molecule in the gas state averaged out over lots of similar molecules, such as the alkanes. 2/2

(ii) The energy needed to break the bonds is

1 C—C = 347
1 C—O = 358
1 O—H = 464
5 C—H = 2065
O=O   498
 Total = 3732 kJ

The energy given out when the new bonds are formed is
4 C=O = 2984
6 H—O = 2784
 Total = 5768
Enthalpy change = 5768 − 3732 = 2036 kJ   1/3

All the bonds broken are correctly identified, but the coefficient of 3 for oxygen has not been used. The calculation is correct for the bonds formed, but the subtraction has been done the wrong way round.

(iii) Ethanol has a formula mass of 46
so in 1 g of ethanol there are 1/46 = 0.217 moles
Heat produced is 2036 × 0.217 = 442 kJ
Octane has a formula mass of 114
so in 1 g of octane there are 1/114 = 0.00877 moles
Heat produced is 5471 × 0.00877 = 48.0 kJ   1/2

Although correct methods have been used, and credit would have been given for using an incorrect value for ethanol from the previous part, an arithmetic error has been made. The amount of ethanol has been written down as 0.217 instead of 0.0217, probably an incorrect reading of the calculator. The two formula masses are correct though.

This answer achieved 7/7

The two vital points (breaking a bond in a gaseous molecule, and the idea of **averaging**) are both included.

(i) The energy required to break a bond in a gaseous molecule, averaged from other values from similar compounds. 2/2

(ii) $\Delta H = \Sigma$ bonds broken $- \Sigma$ bonds formed
$= 347 + 358 + 464 + (5 \times 413) + (3 \times 498)$
$- (4 \times 746) - (6 \times 464)$
$= 4728 - 5768$
$= -1040$ kJ   3/3

This answer correctly shows the expression to be used, then shows the working needed to get to the right answer.

Both relative formula mass values have been correctly calculated (although to the nearest whole number—this was not penalized) and the correct method has been used in both cases.

(iii) For ethanol, heat produced is $\frac{1040 \times 1}{46} = 22.6$ kJ

For octane, heat produced is $\frac{5471 \times 1}{114} = 47.99$ kJ   2/2

3. The standard enthalpy change of three combustion reactions is given below in kJ.

$$2C_2H_6(g) + 7O_2(g) \rightarrow 4CO_2(g) + 6H_2O(l) \qquad \Delta H^\ominus = -3120$$
$$2H_2(g) + O_2(g) \rightarrow 2H_2O(l) \qquad \Delta H^\ominus = -572$$
$$C_2H_4(g) + 3O_2(g) \rightarrow 2CO_2(g) + 2H_2O(l) \qquad \Delta H^\ominus = -1411$$

Based on the above information, calculate the standard change in enthalpy, $\Delta H^\ominus$, for the following reaction.

$$C_2H_6(g) \rightarrow C_2H_4(g) + H_2(g) \qquad \qquad [4]$$

[Taken from paper 2, November 2009]

How do I approach the question?

You are given three balanced equations with their $\Delta H^\ominus$ values and have to calculate the $\Delta H^\ominus$ value for a fourth equation. Note that all the formulas in the fourth equation are to be found in the other three. There is more than one way to tackle this sort of question, and the best way for you will be the one your teacher has used.

One method you could use in this question is to consider each of the three equations in turn and compare it with the fourth one. You may need to rewrite an equation in reverse so that a formula appears on the same side as in the fourth one. You may also need to multiply or divide an equation and its $\Delta H^\ominus$ value so that you have the same coefficients as in the fourth equation.

If you now add the three equations together (with any changed coefficients and $\Delta H^\ominus$ values) and cancel out all formulas that are on both sides, you should end up with the fourth equation, and with the right numerical answer.

What are the key areas of the syllabus?

- Applying Hess's law

This answer achieved 0/4

By just adding the three numbers together, the student shows no understanding of how to tackle this question.

| $-3120 - 572 - 1411 = -5103\,kJ$ | 0/4 |

This answer achieved 2/4

The student seems to understand the need to reverse some equations, but has not considered that sometimes the coefficients need altering as well. Only the third equation is correct (reversed but coefficients unchanged), but the answer is also worth a mark because a partly correct method has been used and the answer follows correctly from the mixture of right and wrong values.

$$2C_2H_6 + 7O_2 \rightarrow 4CO_2 + 6H_2O \qquad \Delta H = -3120\,kJ$$
$$2H_2O \rightarrow 2H_2 + O_2 \qquad \Delta H = +572\,kJ$$
$$2CO_2 + 2H_2O \rightarrow C_2H_4 + 3O_2 \qquad \Delta H = +1411\,kJ$$
$$Answer = -1137\,kJ \qquad 2/4$$

This answer achieved 4/4

Many students have problems with questions of this type, but here it is clear that the student knows how to do this calculation. Very clear working is shown for every step and the final answer is correct (including sign and units).

First equation divided by 2:
$$C_2H_6 + 3\tfrac{1}{2}O_2 \rightarrow 2CO_2 + 3H_2O \qquad \Delta H = -1560$$

Second equation reversed and divided by 2:
$$H_2O \rightarrow H_2 + \tfrac{1}{2}O_2 \qquad \Delta H = +286$$

Third equation reversed:
$$2CO_2 + 2H_2O \rightarrow C_2H_4 + 3O_2 \qquad \Delta H = +1411$$

Adding the equations:
$$C_2H_6 + 3\tfrac{1}{2}O_2 + H_2O + 2CO_2 + 2H_2O \rightarrow 2CO_2 + 3H_2O + H_2 + \tfrac{1}{2}O_2 + C_2H_4 + 3O_2$$

Cancelling out gives:
$$C_2H_6 \rightarrow C_2H_4 + H_2 \qquad \Delta H = +137\,kJ \qquad 4/4$$

10. Kinetics

Rate of reaction

You should know:

- that to measure reaction rate we need to measure the appearance of a product or the disappearance of a reactant by measuring a change in concentration

- suitable methods to measure change in concentration include collecting a gas using a gas syringe and measuring the change in mass using an electronic balance.

You should be able to:

- interpret and sketch graphs of concentration change, volume and mass against time, where time will be on the *x* axis.

Be prepared

- Reaction rates will usually have units of $mol\,dm^{-3}\,s^{-1}$, but could also be $g\,min^{-1}$, for example, depending on what is being measured (concentration or mass) and how long the interval of time is.

Key definitions

- Rate of reaction is the change (Δ) in concentration of a reactant or product divided by time:

$$\frac{\Delta[\text{reactant}]}{\text{time}} \text{ or } \frac{\Delta[\text{product}]}{\text{time}}$$

Example

Equal masses of powdered calcium carbonate were added to separate solutions of hydrochloric acid. The calcium carbonate was in excess. The volume of carbon dioxide produced was measured at regular intervals. Which curves best represent the evolution of carbon dioxide against time for the acid solutions shown in the table below?

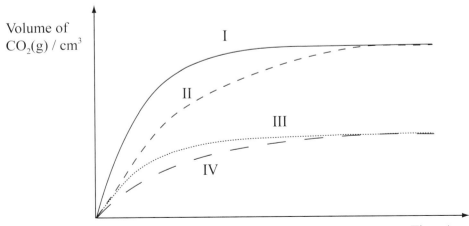

Rate of reaction (continued)

	25 cm³ of 2 mol dm⁻³ HCl	50 cm³ of 1 mol dm⁻³ HCl	25 cm³ of 1 mol dm⁻³ HCl
A.	I	III	IV
B.	I	IV	III
C.	I	II	III
D.	II	I	III

Answer C is correct.

To answer the question, you need to highlight the important information. It states that in all cases calcium carbonate is in excess, so the amount of HCl(aq) will be limiting the reaction. So curves III and IV will be produced when there are fewer moles of

acid, so when there are 25 cm³ of 1 mol dm⁻³. The fastest reaction, I, will be when the acid is most concentrated, so when we have 25 cm³ of 2 mol dm⁻³ HCl(aq). This means the correct response must be C.

Collision theory and activation energy

You should know:

- the kinetic theory states that all particles above $0 K$ ($-273°C$) are moving and that temperature is proportional to the kinetic (movement) energy of particles in a substance

- at higher temperatures particles have more energy and are moving faster

- particles need to collide with enough energy (more than the activation energy E_a) and with the correct geometry for a reaction to occur

- when we increase the frequency of collisions, we increase the reaction rate

- the rate constant k in a reaction will increase with increasing temperature T

- a catalyst also increases the reaction rate by providing an alternative pathway for the reaction that has a lower E_a

- catalysts enable reactions to occur at a lower temperature, and are not used up in the reaction.

You should be able to:

- predict how changing the conditions in a reaction will affect the reaction rate

- explain that decreasing particle size increases surface area, increases frequency of collisions and so increases rate of reaction

- explain that increasing concentration (and pressure) increases frequency of collisions and so increases reaction rate

- explain that increasing temperature increases frequency of collisions but, more importantly, increases the success rate of collisions, as more particles have $E > E_a$.

Be prepared

- Make sure you can sketch the Maxwell–Boltzmann energy distribution curve showing the effect of changing temperature and also the effect of using a catalyst, and remember to label the axes. Remember that this is not the same as an enthalpy level diagram.

Key definitions

- The activation energy is the minimum amount of energy needed for a reaction to occur.

- Rate of reaction $= \dfrac{\Delta[\text{products}]}{\text{time}}$ or $\dfrac{\Delta[\text{reactants}]}{\text{time}}$

Collision theory and activation energy (continued)

Example

(a) Draw a graph to show the distribution of energies in a sample of gas molecules. Label the axes and label your curve T_1. Using the same axes, draw a second curve to represent the distribution of energies at a **higher** temperature. Label this curve T_2.

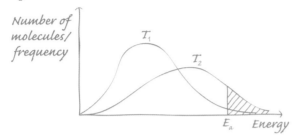

To answer the question, it is essential that you label both axes of the curve and make sure that the curve at the higher temperature is to the right of and lower than the other one. You should try to ensure that the area under each curve is the same, because this represents the number of molecules, which also should be the same. Also, you should indicate the activation energy, E_a.

(b) State and explain, with reference to your graph, what happens to the rate of a reaction when the temperature is increased.

As the temperature increases, so does the reaction rate. This is because more molecules now have energy equal to or greater than the activation energy E_a, that is $E \geq E_a$.

---

4. (a) Define the term *activation energy*, E_a. [1]

(b) State **two** conditions necessary for a reaction to take place between two reactant particles. [2]

(c) Sketch an enthalpy level diagram to describe the effect of a catalyst on an *exothermic* reaction. [3]

[Taken from paper 2, time zone 2, May 2009]

How do I approach the question?

(a) You just need to use the right words to indicate your understanding of the concept.

(b) You need to state two essential points of the collision theory for 1 mark each.

(c) You need to sketch an enthalpy level diagram that shows clearly the effect of the catalyst. Although you need to draw a diagram, not a graph, it is important to label the vertical line. Remember that whether the reaction is exothermic or endothermic decides which of the reactants or products line is higher. Also, when labelling activation energy, remember that it is not a horizontal line, but a vertical distance. Avoid the common error of sketching a graph showing a Maxwell–Boltzmann energy distribution.

What are the key areas of the syllabus?

- Definition of activation energy
- Collision theory
- Enthalpy level diagrams

This answer achieved 1/6

This answer is more like an attempt at explaining the meaning of "endothermic" and does not refer to activation energy.

(a) The energy taken in by substances during a reaction.　　0/1

(b) The molecules must hit each other and with a lot of force.　　1/2

Although the idea of particles colliding is there, the statement about a lot of force is not close enough to the idea of needing energy greater than the activation energy for a further mark to be awarded.

(c)　　0/3

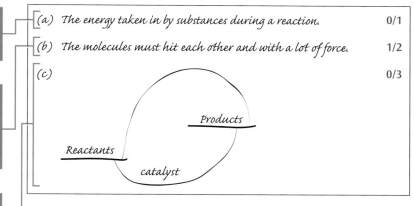

There is nothing of value in this answer. Although there are two lines labelled reactants and products, they are the wrong way round for an exothermic reaction and the catalyst is not correctly shown.

This answer achieved 3/6

This is correct and the key points of energy, molecules and reaction are included.

(a) The energy needed for molecules to react when they collide.　　1/1

(b) The molecules must collide with each other and with the right orientation so the bonds can break.　　2/2

Two points are correctly covered—the ideas of collision and orientation.

(c)　　0/3

CATALYST

REACTANTS

PRODUCTS

Although the diagram seems to contain some valid points, it lacks some key features. The *y* and *x* axes are not labelled, the horizontal line at the top is not described, and there is no reference to activation energy.

This answer achieved 5/6

This is correct and the key points of energy, molecules and reaction are included.

This is correct and the key points of energy, molecules and reaction are included.

Two points are correctly covered—the ideas of collision and orientation.

The diagram and the two curves are correctly labelled, but the activation energy is shown as a point near the top of the curve instead of as the vertical distance from the reactants.

(a) The minimum energy molecules must have to react when they collide. 1/1

(b) When molecules collide they must have a certain energy called the activation energy so that they will react. They must also collide with the correct collision geometry. 2/2

(c) 2/3

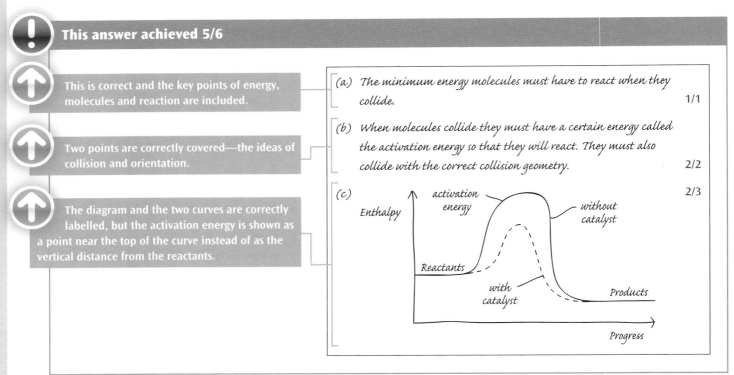

(c) A solution of hydrogen peroxide, H_2O_2, is added to a solution of sodium iodide, NaI, acidified with hydrochloric acid, HCl. The yellow colour of the iodine, I_2, can be used to determine the rate of reaction.

$$H_2O_2\,(aq) + 2NaI\,(aq) + 2HCl\,(aq) \rightarrow 2NaCl\,(aq) + I_2\,(aq) + 2H_2O\,(l)$$

The experiment is repeated with some changes to the reaction conditions. For each of the changes that follow, predict, stating a reason, its effect on the rate of reaction.

(i)   The concentration of H_2O_2 is increased at constant temperature.   *[2]*

(ii)   The solution of NaI is prepared from a fine powder instead of large crystals.   *[2]*

(d)   Explain why the rate of a reaction increases when the temperature of the system increases.   *[3]*

[Taken from paper 2, November 2009]

How do I approach the question?

(c)   In part (i), you need to make the prediction, then explain it by using the collision theory. It is always better to refer to particles, rather than to atoms, molecules or ions, because referring to atoms if the particles are ions sometimes loses a mark. A common error to be aware of is writing about more collisions with no reference to time.

In part (ii), beware of jumping to the same conclusion that most students did. Think about whether the two NaI solutions will react differently because of how they were prepared.

(d)   When explaining the effect of changing temperature on reaction rate, always remember that there are two different factors involved. The minor one is the change in frequency of collisions; the major one is the change in the number of collisions where the particles have energy greater than the activation energy.

What are the key areas of the syllabus?

- Using the collision theory to explain the effects of changing conditions on the rate of a reaction

This answer achieved 2/7

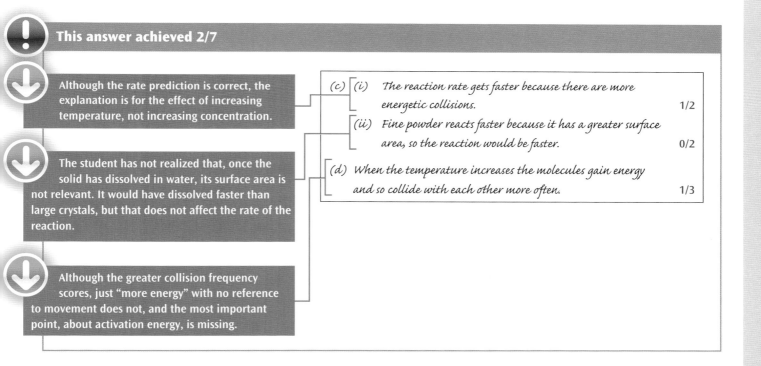

Although the rate prediction is correct, the explanation is for the effect of increasing temperature, not increasing concentration.

The student has not realized that, once the solid has dissolved in water, its surface area is not relevant. It would have dissolved faster than large crystals, but that does not affect the rate of the reaction.

Although the greater collision frequency scores, just "more energy" with no reference to movement does not, and the most important point, about activation energy, is missing.

(c)   (i)   The reaction rate gets faster because there are more energetic collisions.   1/2

(ii)   Fine powder reacts faster because it has a greater surface area, so the reaction would be faster.   0/2

(d)   When the temperature increases the molecules gain energy and so collide with each other more often.   1/3

This answer achieved 3/7

Although the rate prediction is correct, the explanation lacks the essential reference to time or frequency. Stating that there are more collisions is never enough without a reference to frequency or time. In this case, it must be more frequent collisions (or the equivalent, such as "the particles collide more often" or "there are more collisions per second between particles").

(c) (i) The rate will be faster because the particles collide more.   1/2

(ii) The reaction would be faster because the surface area of a fine powder is greater than that of large crystals, so there are more collisions.   0/2

(d) The reacting particles move faster and collide more often, so the rate increases.   2/3

Two valid points are made—the faster molecules and the more frequent collisions—but there is no reference to activation energy or more energetic collisions.

This answer achieved 7/7

The prediction of rate is correct, and the explanation includes the essential word "frequently".

(c) (i) Increasing the concentration means that the particles collide more frequently, so the rate increases.   2/2

(ii) The rate would be the same because once the solution is prepared then the size of the particles does not matter.   2/2

This student has realized that particle size is not relevant once the solution has been prepared.

(d) When the temperature increases the reacting particles have more kinetic energy so they move faster and collide more often. Also more particles have energy above the activation energy, so more collisions result in reactions.   3/3

The three essential points are included in this answer: greater kinetic energy, increased collision frequency and a correct reference to activation energy.

11. Equilibrium

Dynamic equilibrium

You should know:

- at equilibrium the macroscopic properties (concentration, colour and so on) will remain the same but on a microscopic level particles are moving between being reactants and products and vice versa

- at equilibrium the rate of the forward reaction is equal to the rate of the reverse reaction.

The position of equilibrium

You should know:

- Le Chatelier's principle states that a system in equilibrium will oppose any change made to it

- an increase in concentration of reactants will shift equilibrium to the products

- an increase in concentration of products will shift equilibrium to the reactants

- an increase in temperature will shift equilibrium to the products if it is an endothermic reaction and to the reactants if it is an exothermic reaction

- an increase in pressure will favour the side of the equation with the most moles of gas

- a catalyst has no effect on the position of equilibrium or on the value of the equilibrium constant, because it speeds up the rate of forward and reverse reactions equally

- if $K_c \gg 1$ (K_c is much bigger than 1) then the reaction will go almost to completion, and if $K_c \ll 1$ (K_c is much smaller than 1) the reaction will hardly happen.

You should be able to:

- work out the equilibrium constant expression K_c from the chemical equation (remember that it is products over reactants), and the value will not have any units.

Be prepared

- Remember that, when writing the K_c expression, you must use square brackets to indicate concentrations, for example [X].

- You need to understand how the concepts of equilibrium and kinetics are applied to industrial processes such as the Haber process to make ammonia.

Example

(a) $I_2(g) + 3Cl_2(g) \rightleftharpoons 2ICl_3(g)$

What is the equilibrium constant expression for the reaction above?

A. $K_c = \dfrac{[ICl_3]}{[I_2][Cl_2]}$

B. $K_c = \dfrac{2[ICl_3]}{3[I_2][Cl_2]}$

C. $K_c = \dfrac{2[ICl_3]}{[I_2] + 3[Cl_2]}$

D. $K_c = \dfrac{[ICl_3]^2}{[I_2][Cl_2]^3}$

Correct answer is D.

The constant is formed from products divided by reactants, and the concentration of each is raised to the power of

The position of equilibrium (continued)

the coefficient (big numbers in front of substances) in the balanced equation. So $3Cl_2$ becomes $[Cl_2]^3$ and so on. Therefore, the correct answer is D. If (...) was used instead of [...] in a written answer, it would be incorrect, and a mark would be lost.

(b) In the reaction below

$$N_2(g) + 3H_2(g) \rightleftharpoons 2NH_3(g) \qquad \Delta H = -92\,kJ$$

which of the following changes will not increase the amount of ammonia at equilibrium?

   I.   Increasing the temperature
   II. Increasing the pressure
   III. Adding a catalyst

A.   I and II only
B.   I and III only
C.   II and III only
D.   I, II and III

Correct answer is B.

You should know this reaction well, as it is the Haber process. Increasing temperature will not increase yield, because this is an exothermic reaction (it will however increase rate). Pressure increases yield though, as 4 moles of gas make 2 moles of gas. Adding a catalyst will increase the rate but has no effect on yield, so the correct answer is B.

---

5.   (a)   Consider the following equilibrium.

$$2SO_2(g) + O_2(g) \rightleftharpoons 2SO_3(g) \qquad \Delta H^\ominus = -198\ kJ\ mol^{-1}$$

(i)   Deduce the equilibrium constant expression, K_c, for the reaction.   *[1]*

(ii)   State and explain the effect of increasing the temperature on the yield of sulfur trioxide.   *[2]*

(iii)   State the effect of a catalyst on the value of K_c.   *[1]*

(iv)   State and explain the effect of a catalyst on the position of equilibrium.   *[2]*

[Taken from paper 2, time zone 2, May 2009]

How do I approach the question?

(i)   You just have to write the equilibrium constant for the reaction.

(ii)   You should apply Le Chatelier's principle for a change in temperature.

(iii)   You need to understand the effect of a catalyst on an equilibrium.

(iv)   Again, you need to understand the effect of a catalyst on an equilibrium.

What are the key areas of the syllabus?

- Chemical equilibrium
- K_c expressions
- Applying Le Chatelier's principle

This answer achieved 1/6

The coefficients from the equation should not have been included inside the square brackets.

(i) $K_c = \dfrac{[2SO_3]^2}{[2SO_2]^2[O_2]}$ 0/1

The prediction is wrong and, although the increase in temperature does cause an increase in rate, this does not explain a change in yield.

(ii) When the temperature is increased the yield of SO_3 increases because the reaction speeds up.   0/2

(iii) Catalysts do not affect the equilibrium constant.   1/1

This is correct—note that the question asked for a statement and an explanation was not needed.

(iv) The equilibrium moves to the right because the yield of SO_3 has increased.   0/2

This is incorrect—catalysts do not affect the position of equilibrium.

This answer achieved 3/6

The + sign should not have been included on the bottom line of the expression.

(i) $K_c = \dfrac{[SO_3]^2}{[SO_2]^2 + [O_2]}$ 0/1

The prediction and its explanation are both correct.

(ii) When the temperature goes up the equilibrium shifts to the left because the reaction is exothermic. This means the yield of SO_3 goes down.   2/2

(iii) Catalysts do not affect the equilibrium constant.   1/1

This is correct—the question asked for a statement and an explanation was not needed.

(iv) A catalyst speeds up the forward reaction more than the reverse reaction so the equilibrium moves to the right.   0/2

This is incorrect—the catalyst speeds up both forward and reverse reactions equally, so there is no effect on the position of equilibrium.

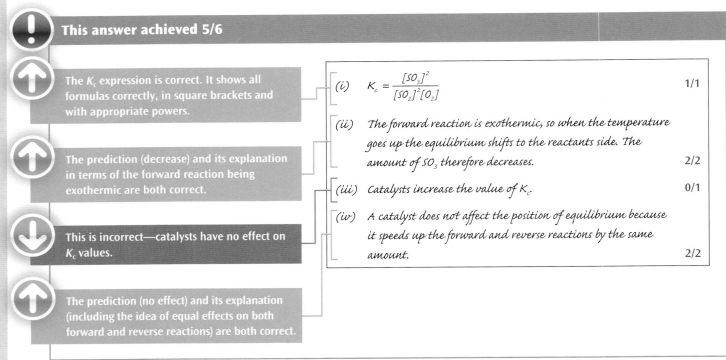

This answer achieved 5/6

The K_c expression is correct. It shows all formulas correctly, in square brackets and with appropriate powers.

The prediction (decrease) and its explanation in terms of the forward reaction being exothermic are both correct.

This is incorrect—catalysts have no effect on K_c values.

The prediction (no effect) and its explanation (including the idea of equal effects on both forward and reverse reactions) are both correct.

(i) $\quad K_c = \dfrac{[SO_3]^2}{[SO_2]^2[O_2]}$ ⟶ 1/1

(ii) The forward reaction is exothermic, so when the temperature goes up the equilibrium shifts to the reactants side. The amount of SO_3 therefore decreases. ⟶ 2/2

(iii) Catalysts increase the value of K_c. ⟶ 0/1

(iv) A catalyst does not affect the position of equilibrium because it speeds up the forward and reverse reactions by the same amount. ⟶ 2/2

---

5. (a) Consider the following reaction taking place at 375 °C in a 1.00 dm³ closed container.

$$Cl_2(g) + SO_2(g) \rightleftharpoons SO_2Cl_2(g) \qquad \Delta H^{\ominus} = -84.5 \text{ kJ}$$

(i) Deduce the equilibrium constant expression, K_c, for the reaction. *[1]*

(ii) If the temperature of the reaction is changed to 300 °C, predict, stating a reason in each case, whether the equilibrium concentration of SO_2Cl_2 and the value of K_c will increase or decrease. *[3]*

(iii) If the volume of the container is changed to 1.50 dm³, predict, stating a reason in each case, how this will affect the equilibrium concentration of SO_2Cl_2 and the value of K_c. *[3]*

(iv) Suggest, stating a reason, how the addition of a catalyst at constant pressure and temperature will affect the equilibrium concentration of SO_2Cl_2. *[2]*

[Taken from paper 2, November 2009]

How do I approach the question?

(i) You need to be able to write the equilibrium constant expression carefully, including square brackets and any coefficients from the equation in the right places (although there are none in this example). Note that state symbols should ideally be shown, but there is not usually any penalty for leaving them out.

(ii) You need to apply Le Chatelier's principle to an exothermic reaction to predict and explain what happens to the position of equilibrium **and** to the value of K_c. These are related but not the same and should be answered separately even if the explanation is the same for both of them

(iii) You need to apply Le Chatelier's principle to a reaction in which the volume of the container has been increased—this is equivalent to decreasing the pressure. Remember that, when giving a reason, there must be some reference to the molecules being gaseous.

(iv) You need to state the effect of the catalyst on both forward and reverse reactions—it increases them equally. The predictions about concentrations and the equilibrium constant are always the same.

What are the key areas of the syllabus?

- Deducing an equilibrium constant
- Applying Le Chatelier's principle to reversible reactions

This answer achieved 0/9

Although all the formulas are correct and the right way round, the + sign means that no mark can be awarded.

This is a wrong prediction, there is no reason given, and the question about K_c has not been answered.

Again, this is a wrong prediction, no reason is given and there is no mention of K_c.

The statement about the rate increasing is correct, but the question is about equilibrium, not rate.

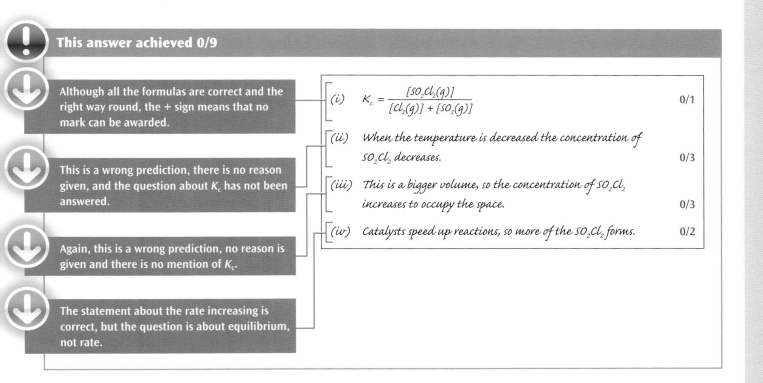

(i) $K_c = \dfrac{[SO_2Cl_2(g)]}{[Cl_2(g)] + [SO_2(g)]}$ 0/1

(ii) When the temperature is decreased the concentration of SO_2Cl_2 decreases.   0/3

(iii) This is a bigger volume, so the concentration of SO_2Cl_2 increases to occupy the space.   0/3

(iv) Catalysts speed up reactions, so more of the SO_2Cl_2 forms.   0/2

This answer achieved 4/9

This is a correct expression—formulas are correct and in the right places.

Although there is no mention of K_c, the other prediction and reason are both correct.

The statement about K_c is wrong, and although the lower concentration of all the molecules has not been worked out by Le Chatelier's principle, it is a correct statement about SO_2Cl_2.

The only correct statement is about K_c being the same, but as this was not asked for in the question, no mark can be awarded.

(i) $K_c = \dfrac{[SO_2Cl_2]}{[Cl_2][SO_2]}$ — 1/1

(ii) The temperature goes down and the reaction is exothermic, so the equilibrium shifts to the right, so the concentration of SO_2Cl_2 goes up. — 2/3

(iii) Increasing the volume means that all the molecules have a lower concentration, so K_c decreases. — 1/3

(iv) Adding a catalyst speeds up the forward reaction more than the reverse reaction so the equilibrium moves to the right, although the K_c is the same. — 0/2

This answer achieved 8/9

This is a correct expression—all formulas are correct, in the right places and with square brackets used.

Two correct predictions and a relevant explanation are given.

This is a good answer, but there is one key point left out—the reference to the molecules being gaseous—so a mark is lost.

A correct prediction (no effect) and a relevant explanation (reference to equal effects on both forward and reverse rates) are both given.

(i) $K_c = \dfrac{[SO_2Cl_2]}{[SO_2][Cl_2]}$ — 1/1

(ii) If the temperature is decreased, then the position of equilibrium will shift to the right because the reaction is exothermic (negative ΔH value). Both $[SO_2Cl_2]$ and K_c will increase. — 3/3

(iii) The volume has increased, so the reaction shifts in the direction which gives more molecules. This is to the left, so $[SO_2Cl_2]$ decreases. Only temperature affects the value of K_c, so this stays the same. — 2/3

(iv) Catalysts have the effect of speeding up the forward and reverse reactions by the same amount, so there is no effect on the concentration of SO_2Cl_2. — 2/2

12. Acids and bases

Theories and properties of acids and bases

You should know:

- acids turn universal indicator and litmus red
- acids are neutralized by bases
- acids form a salt and water with metal oxides
- acids form a salt, water and carbon dioxide gas with carbonates and hydrogencarbonates
- acids react with metals to produce a salt and hydrogen gas
- when bases dissolve in water they are called alkalis.

You should be able to:

- identify Brønsted–Lowry acids and bases in a reaction, and remember that the conjugate pair will differ by H^+, for example CH_3COOH and CH_3COO^-
- identify Lewis acids and bases in a reaction, and remember that all Brønsted–Lowry acids and bases are also Lewis acids and bases
- remember that substances that are only acids and bases according to the Lewis theory will not contain H^+ and are often transition metal or aluminium compounds in solution (so, for example, HCl is a Brønsted–Lowry acid and also a Lewis acid, but $AlCl_3$ is only a Lewis acid as it does not have an H^+ to donate).

Be prepared

- Practise writing equations with hydrochloric (HCl), sulfuric (H_2SO_4), nitric (HNO_3) and ethanoic (CH_3CHOOH) acids with a variety of metals, and basic compounds such as NaOH or CuO.

Key definitions

- A Brønsted–Lowry acid is a proton (H^+) donor and a Brønsted–Lowry base is a proton acceptor.
- A Lewis acid is an electron pair acceptor and a Lewis base is an electron pair donor.

Example

(a) Which **one** of the following species can act as both a Brønsted–Lowry acid and base in aqueous solution?

- A. CH_3COOH
- B. NO_3^-
- C. $H_2PO_4^-$
- D. OH^-

C is correct.

The wording means that the species can both gain and lose a proton (H^+) to make a stable product. Species A cannot gain a proton, and B cannot lose a proton. This leaves C and D as possible correct answers. D will not lose H^+ in solution to form O^{2-}, so this leaves C as the correct answer. $H_2PO_4^-$ can lose H^+ to form HPO_4^{2-} and can gain a proton to form H_3PO_4 (phosphoric acid).

(b) Which equation represents an acid–base reaction according to the Lewis theory **but not** according to the Brønsted–Lowry theory?

- A. $CO_3^{2-}(aq) + 2H^+(aq) \rightarrow H_2O(l) + CO_2(g)$
- B. $Cu^{2+}(aq) + 4NH_3(aq) \rightarrow Cu(NH_3)_4^{2+}(aq)$
- C. $BaO(s) + H_2O(l) \rightarrow Ba^{2+}(aq) + 2OH^-(aq)$
- D. $NH_3(g) + HCl(g) \rightarrow NH_4Cl(s)$

B is correct.

In this question we are looking for an equation where we do not have proton transfer taking place. This quickly makes B the correct answer. In these questions the answer is often the one including a transition metal ion.

Theories and properties of acids and bases (continued)

(c) In which reaction is $H_2PO_4^-$(aq) acting as a Brønsted–Lowry base?

A. $H_2PO_4^-$(aq) + NH_3(aq) → HPO_4^{2-}(aq) + NH_4^+(aq)

B. $H_2PO_4^-$(aq) + OH^-(aq) → HPO_4^{2-}(aq) + H_2O(l)

C. $H_2PO_4^-$(aq) + $C_2H_5NH_2$(aq) → HPO_4^{2-}(aq) + $C_2H_5NH_3^+$(aq)

D. $H_2PO_4^-$(aq) + CH_3COOH(aq) → H_3PO_4(aq) + CH_3COO^-(aq)

D is correct.

Here we are looking for $H_2PO_4^-$ acting as a proton acceptor and so forming H_3PO_4, which makes the correct answer D.

Strong and weak acids and bases, and the pH scale

You should know:

- weak acids are only partially dissociated and because of this they have a low concentration of ions, so they do not conduct electricity as well as strong acids, which are fully dissociated into their ions

- strong acids can be distinguished from weak acids of the same concentration by comparing their conductivities

- strong acids can be distinguished from weak acids of the same concentration by comparing their reactions with magnesium or calcium carbonate—the strong acid will react more rapidly, leading to a quicker evolution of gas

- strong acids will have a lower pH, which can be measured using a pH meter or universal indicator

- the pH scale gives a measure of relative acidity or basicity, and on this scale pH 1 is a strong acid, pH 7 is neutral and pH 14 is strongly alkaline.

You should be able to:

- work out the change in $[H^+]$ when the pH changes, as each pH unit change is equivalent to a 10-fold change in $[H^+]$, so an increase in pH of 1 means a decrease in $[H^+]$ of 10, and a decrease in pH of 3 means an increase in $[H^+]$ of 1000

- identify which substances are more acidic or alkaline from their pH values.

Be prepared

- Rain water is naturally acidic due to CO_2 in the air. When the pollutants SO_2 and NO_x react with rain water, this leads to "acid rain". Acid rain reacts with limestone buildings, eroding them, and changes the pH of soil and lakes.

- Strong acids are HCl, H_2SO_4 and HNO_3, and examples of weak acids are carbonic acid (HCOOH) and the carboxylic acids such as CH_3COOH. The strong bases (alkalis) are the hydroxides of group 1 (NaOH and so on) and barium $(Ba(OH)_2)$, and the weak bases are ammonia (NH_3) and the amines, for example methylamine CH_3NH_2.

Example

Ethanoic acid, CH_3COOH, is a weak acid.

(a) Define the term *weak acid* and state the equation for the reaction of ethanoic acid with water.

A weak acid is one that is only partially dissociated.

$CH_3COOH + H_2O \rightleftharpoons CH_3COO^- + H_3O^+$

This is the correct equation, and it is important that you include the equilibrium sign.

(b) Vinegar, which contains ethanoic acid, can be used to clean deposits of calcium carbonate from the elements of electric kettles. State the equation for the reaction of ethanoic acid with calcium carbonate, including state symbols.

CH_3COOH(aq) + $CaCO_3$(s) → $(CH_3COO)_2Ca$(aq) + H_2O(l) + CO_2(g)

The important thing to notice here is that there is no equilibrium sign—this reaction will go to completion. Also, ethanoic acid and the salt it forms, calcium ethanoate, are both soluble in water. The formula of calcium ethanoate is worked out using the formulas of the ions (Ca^{2+} because calcium is in group 2, and remembering that the ethanoate ion has a single negative charge).

6. (a) The equations of two acid-base reactions are given below.

Reaction **A** $NH_3(aq) + H_2O(l) \rightleftharpoons \underline{NH_4^+(aq)} + OH^-(aq)$

The reaction mixture in **A** consists mainly of reactants because the equilibrium lies to the left.

Reaction **B** $NH_2^-(aq) + H_2O(l) \rightleftharpoons \underline{NH_3(aq)} + OH^-(aq)$

The reaction mixture in **B** consists mainly of products because the equilibrium lies to the right.

(i) For each of the reactions **A** and **B**, deduce whether water is acting as an acid or a base and explain your answer. [2]

(ii) In reaction **B**, identify the stronger base, NH_2^- or OH^- and explain your answer. [2]

(iii) In reactions **A** and **B**, identify the stronger acid, NH_4^+ or NH_3 (underlined) and explain your answer. [2]

(b) Describe **two** different experimental methods to distinguish between aqueous solutions of a strong base and a weak base. [5]

(c) Two acidic solutions, **X** and **Y**, of equal concentrations have pH values of 2 and 6 respectively.

(i) Calculate the hydrogen ion concentrations in the two solutions and identify the stronger acid. [2]

(ii) Determine the ratio of the hydrogen ion concentrations in the two solutions **X** and **Y**. [1]

(d) (i) Define a Lewis acid and state an example that is not a Brønsted-Lowry acid. [2]

(ii) Draw structural formulas to represent the reaction between the Lewis acid named in (d) (i) and a Lewis base and identify the nature of the bond formed in the product. [4]

[Taken from paper 2, November 2009]

How do I approach the question?

(a) Each part needs an understanding of the Brønsted–Lowry theory and its application.

(b) You need to state two suitable methods to distinguish strong and weak bases in solution, including the result for each base. As the question does not mention that the solutions are of equal concentration, the answer should.

(c) You need an understanding of the relationship between [H⁺] and pH.

(d) You need to understand the Lewis theory of acids and bases and apply it in an example of your own choice—always choose a straightforward one that you are familiar with. There are no extra marks for unusual examples and you are more likely to make a mistake.

What are the key areas of the syllabus?

- The Brønsted–Lowry and Lewis theories of acids and bases
- Distinguishing weak and strong acids and bases
- The pH scale

This answer achieved 5/20

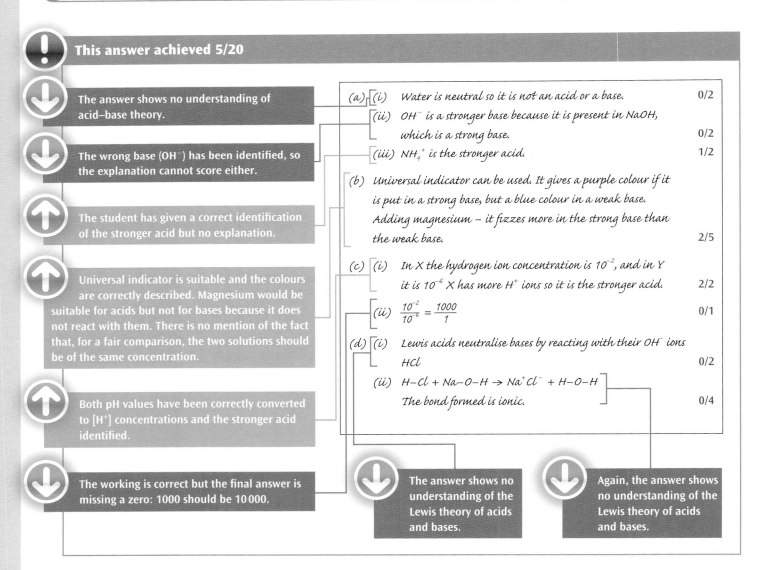

The answer shows no understanding of acid–base theory.

The wrong base (OH⁻) has been identified, so the explanation cannot score either.

The student has given a correct identification of the stronger acid but no explanation.

Universal indicator is suitable and the colours are correctly described. Magnesium would be suitable for acids but not for bases because it does not react with them. There is no mention of the fact that, for a fair comparison, the two solutions should be of the same concentration.

Both pH values have been correctly converted to [H⁺] concentrations and the stronger acid identified.

The working is correct but the final answer is missing a zero: 1000 should be 10 000.

(a) (i) Water is neutral so it is not an acid or a base. 0/2

(ii) OH⁻ is a stronger base because it is present in NaOH, which is a strong base. 0/2

(iii) NH_4^+ is the stronger acid. 1/2

(b) Universal indicator can be used. It gives a purple colour if it is put in a strong base, but a blue colour in a weak base. Adding magnesium – it fizzes more in the strong base than the weak base. 2/5

(c) (i) In X the hydrogen ion concentration is 10^{-2}, and in Y it is 10^{-6} X has more H⁺ ions so it is the stronger acid. 2/2

(ii) $\dfrac{10^{-2}}{10^{-6}} = \dfrac{1000}{1}$ 0/1

(d) (i) Lewis acids neutralise bases by reacting with their OH⁻ ions
HCl 0/2

(ii) $H–Cl + Na–O–H \rightarrow Na^+Cl^- + H–O–H$
The bond formed is ionic. 0/4

The answer shows no understanding of the Lewis theory of acids and bases.

Again, the answer shows no understanding of the Lewis theory of acids and bases.

This answer achieved 9/20

The behaviour of water as a proton donor has been correctly described.

The wrong base has been identified and no explanation has been given.

The correct base has been identified but no explanation is given.

Both methods are correct and the results are correctly described.

This is the right idea, but X and Y are the wrong way round.

There is nothing correct here. There is no mention of accepting an electron pair, and ammonia is an example of a base, not an acid.

This reaction does not occur, although the reverse reaction could be used to illustrate the Brønsted–Lowry theory, not the Lewis theory.

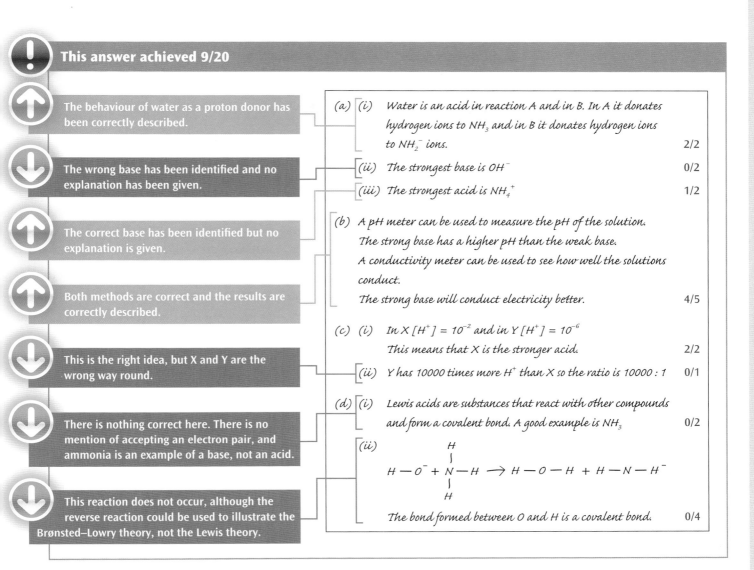

(a) (i) Water is an acid in reaction A and in B. In A it donates hydrogen ions to NH_3 and in B it donates hydrogen ions to NH_2^- ions. — 2/2

(ii) The strongest base is OH^- — 0/2

(iii) The strongest acid is NH_4^+ — 1/2

(b) A pH meter can be used to measure the pH of the solution. The strong base has a higher pH than the weak base. A conductivity meter can be used to see how well the solutions conduct. The strong base will conduct electricity better. — 4/5

(c) (i) In X $[H^+] = 10^{-2}$ and in Y $[H^+] = 10^{-6}$ This means that X is the stronger acid. — 2/2

(ii) Y has 10000 times more H^+ than X so the ratio is 10000 : 1 — 0/1

(d) (i) Lewis acids are substances that react with other compounds and form a covalent bond. A good example is NH_3 — 0/2

(ii) $$H-O^- + N-H \rightarrow H-O-H + H-N-H^-$$ The bond formed between O and H is a covalent bond. — 0/4

This answer achieved 17/20

Water has been correctly identified as an acid in both reactions in terms of its action as a proton donor.

The wrong base has been identified, so the explanation is not relevant.

The ammonium ion has been correctly identified as an acid, and justified by reference to the position of equilibrium.

Although there is no reference to the need for the two solutions to have the same concentration, everything else is correct.

Both pH values have been correctly converted to $[H^+]$ values, then correctly compared.

This is the correct ratio and expressed in the right format, using the colon (:) symbol.

The Lewis theory has been correctly described, with an example.

All the formulas are correct, including the short $\leftarrow$ symbol to represent the coordinate bond with the two electrons supplied by the N atom.

(a) (i) In A, water acts as an acid because it becomes OH^- and gives H^+ to NH_3

In B, it does the same thing only with NH_2^- so it is an acid here as well. **2/2**

(ii) OH^- is the stronger base because the equilibrium lies to the right, where the OH^- ions are. **0/2**

(iii) NH_4^+ is the stronger acid because the equilibrium lies to the left, so it converts many OH^- ions to H_2O molecules. **2/2**

(b) Use a pH meter – a strong base will have a pH about 12–14, but a weak base about 9–11

Test the conductivity – the strong base will conduct electricity better. **4/5**

(c) (i) X has a hydrogen ion concentration of 10^{-2} and Y has 10^{-6}
X is stronger than Y **2/2**

(ii) X has 10000 times more H^+ than Y so the ratio is 10000 : 1 **1/1**

(d) (i) A Lewis acid forms a covalent bond when it reacts with another substance with both electrons coming from the other substance BF_3 is an example. **2/2**

(ii)

$$F-\underset{\underset{F}{|}}{\overset{\overset{F}{|}}{B}} \quad + \quad H-\underset{\underset{H}{|}}{\overset{\overset{H}{|}}{N}}-H \quad \longrightarrow \quad F-\underset{\underset{F}{|}}{\overset{\overset{F}{|}}{B}} \leftarrow \underset{\underset{H}{|}}{\overset{\overset{H}{|}}{N}}-H$$

The bond is called a coordinate bond. **4/4**

13. Oxidation and reduction

Introduction to oxidation and reduction, and redox equations

You should know:

- every element has an oxidation number, which is 0 if it is an unreacted element, and in a compound it will be + or − depending on whether the substance it has joined with is more or less electronegative than it

- the maximum positive oxidation number is the same as the group number and the lowest negative oxidation number occurs when the element gains enough electrons to fill its outer shell, so Br in group 7 can have an oxidation number between +7 and −1

- an oxidation number is not the same as a charge, so Ca^{2+} has an oxidation number of +2 and not 2+.

You should be able to:

- use oxidation numbers to decide if an element has been oxidized, because its oxidation number increases (becomes more positive), or has been reduced, because its oxidation number decreases (becomes more negative)

- name compounds using oxidation numbers using roman numerals, for example, iron(II) oxide for FeO

- write half-equations for reactions, balancing them with electrons (e^-), H^+ and H_2O

- combine half-equations and then balance them by making sure electrons lost = electrons gained.

Be prepared

- There are many redox half-equations in table 14 of the data booklet. These are all written as reduction reactions, and as equilibrium reactions. When you use them, remember to change the equilibrium arrows to a normal arrow, and to write them the other way around if you want an oxidation reaction.

Key definitions

- Oxidation is the loss of electrons and reduction is the gain of electrons. (You could remember this using "OIL RIG".)

- An oxidizing agent causes oxidation and in the process is reduced.

- A reducing agent causes reduction and in the process is oxidized.

Example

(a) What is the coefficient for H^+ when the equation below is balanced?

$$\_\_Pb(s) + \_\_NO_3^-(aq) + \_\_H^+(aq) \rightarrow \_\_Pb^{2+}(aq) + \_\_NO(g) + \_\_H_2O(l)$$

A. 2

B. 4

C. 6

D. 8

The correct answer is D.

When you see an equation like this, always make sure that the electrons are balanced as well as the atoms. Here Pb is becoming Pb^{2+} so is losing two electrons, and NO_3^- is becoming NO, which is a change in oxidation number from +5 to +2, so it has gained three electrons. To balance the electrons, then, you will need three Pb and two NO_3^-. Then to balance the oxygens you will need to have four H_2O, so you will have eight H^+. So the correct answer is D.

Introduction to oxidation and reduction, and redox equations (continued)

(b) When the following equation is balanced, what is the coefficient for Ce^{4+}?

$$\_\_SO_3^{2-}(aq) + \_\_H_2O(l) + \_\_Ce^{4+}(aq) \rightarrow$$
$$\_\_SO_4^{2-}(aq) + \_\_H^+(aq) + \_\_Ce^{3+}(aq)$$

A. 1

B. 2

C. 3

D. 4

The correct answer is B.

Again, you must make sure that the electrons are balanced as well as the atoms. Here Ce^{4+} is becoming Ce^{3+} so is gaining one electron, and SO_3^{2-} is becoming SO_4^{2-}, which is a change in oxidation number from +4 to +6, so it has lost two electrons. To balance the electrons then you need two Ce^{4+} to react with each SO_3^{2-}. So the correct answer is B.

Reactivity

You should know:

- that reactivity depends on how easily electrons are lost or gained

- the most reactive substances are found at either end of the standard electrode potential table (table 14 in data booklet)

- the most reactive metals are at the top and most reactive non-metals at the bottom.

You should be able to:

- work out a reactivity series if given information about how substances react with the same substance, such as oxygen, or with each other

- remember that more reactive substances can displace less reactive substances, for example

$$Fe_2O_3(s) + 2Al(s) \rightarrow 2Fe(s) + Al_2O_3(s)$$

Example

(a) The following reactions are spontaneous as written.

$$Fe(s) + Cd^{2+}(aq) \rightarrow Fe^{2+}(aq) + Cd(s)$$
$$Cd(s) + Sn^{2+}(aq) \rightarrow Cd^{2+}(aq) + Sn(s)$$
$$Sn(s) + Pb^{2+}(aq) \rightarrow Sn^{2+}(aq) + Pb(s)$$

Which of the following pairs will react spontaneously?

I. $Cd(s) + Pb^{2+}(aq)$
II. $Sn(s) + Fe^{2+}(aq)$
III. $Fe(s) + Pb^{2+}(aq)$

A. I and II only

B. I and III only

C. II and III only

D. I, II and III

B is correct.

In this question you need to realize that more reactive metals can displace less reactive metals. From the equations, we can see that reactivity is arranged as Fe > Cd > Sn > Pb. From this we can see that I will occur, II will not occur as Sn is less reactive than Fe, and III will also work. So the correct answer is B.

(b) A part of the reactivity series of metals, in order of decreasing reactivity, is shown below.

> magnesium
> zinc
> iron
> lead
> copper
> silver

If a piece of copper metal were placed in separate solutions of silver nitrate and zinc nitrate:

(i) determine which solution would undergo reaction.

Silver nitrate would undergo reaction.

You are told the reactivity series in the question, so you just need to remember that more reactive metals can displace less reactive metals. Copper is more reactive than silver and less reactive than zinc, so you will see a reaction with silver nitrate.

Reactivity (continued)

(ii) identify the type of chemical change taking place in the copper and write the half-equation for this change.

The chemical change taking place in the copper is oxidation, as it is losing electrons. The half-equation is:

$$Cu\,(s) \rightarrow Cu^{2+}(aq) + 2e^-$$

(iii) state, giving a reason, what visible change would take place in the solutions.

There are two changes taking place that you will see. The solution will change from colourless to blue, as Ag^+ is colourless and Cu^{2+} is blue. Also a greyish silver metal will be deposited.

Voltaic cells

You should know:

- that if two half-cells are connected to a voltmeter and there is a salt bridge between them, they will produce a voltage
- the bigger the difference in reactivity between the half-cells, the greater the voltage
- oxidation occurs at the negative electrode (anode)
- reduction occurs at the positive electrode (cathode).

You should be able to:

- draw a diagram to explain how a voltage is produced and show the direction of electron flow (from more reactive to less reactive).

Be prepared

- Oxidation occurs at the anode and electrons flow from it, so the anode is the negative electrode. Reduction occurs at the cathode, so it is the positive electrode, as it gains the electrons.

Example

(a) What occurs during the operation of a voltaic cell based on the following reaction?

$$Ni(s) + Pb^{2+}(aq) \rightarrow Ni^{2+}(aq) + Pb(s)$$

	External circuit	Ion movement in solution
A.	electrons move from Ni to Pb	$Pb^{2+}(aq)$ move away from $Pb(s)$
B.	electrons move from Ni to Pb	$Pb^{2+}(aq)$ move towards $Pb(s)$
C.	electrons move from Pb to Ni	$Ni^{2+}(aq)$ move away from $Ni(s)$
D.	electrons move from Pb to Ni	$Ni^{2+}(aq)$ move towards $Ni(s)$

The correct answer is B.

In this reaction Ni is losing electrons and Pb^{2+} is gaining them, so electrons move from Ni to Pb in the external circuit. So the answer is A or B. Since $Pb^{2+}(aq)$ is gaining electrons, it must move towards $Pb(s)$ to collect them. So the correct answer is B.

(b) A voltaic cell is made from copper and zinc half-cells. The equation for the reaction occurring in the cell is

$$Zn(s) + Cu^{2+}(aq) \rightarrow Zn^{2+}(aq) + Cu(s)$$

Which statement is correct when the cell produces electricity?

A. Electrons are lost from zinc atoms.

B. The mass of the copper electrode decreases.

C. Electrons flow from the copper half-cell to the zinc half-cell.

D. Negative ions flow through the salt bridge from the zinc half-cell to the copper half-cell.

A is correct.

When the cell is producing electricity, electrons will flow from the more reactive to the less reactive metal—from the metal that oxidizes to the metal that reduces, so from Zn to Cu^{2+}. Based on this, A is correct, as Zn does lose electrons. B is false, as the mass of the copper electrode will increase. C is false, as electrons flow from Zn to Cu. D is false because negative ions would flow towards the Zn cell, as here there is a build-up of positive charge.

Electrolytic cells

You should know:

- electrolysis is the decomposition of an electrolyte by an electric current and it makes elements from compounds

- in an electrolytic cell there is a d.c. power source and not a voltmeter, and there are two electrodes and one electrolyte (there might also be an ammeter or bulb in the circuit)

- electrolysis occurs when the ions can move—so the electrolyte (liquid with ions) must be molten or in aqueous solution.

You should be able to:

- work out what will be produced at each electrode during the electrolysis of a molten salt

- write half-equations for the reactions at each electrode, remembering that metals gain electrons and non-metals lose electrons

- remember that many non-metals form diatomic molecules.

Be prepared

- Remember that electrons flow in the wires and ions flow through the electrolyte.

- Oxidation occurs at the anode and negative ions flow to it, so it is the positive electrode.

- Reduction occurs at the cathode, so it is the negative electrode, as positive ions gain electrons here.

(b) (i) Define *oxidation* in terms of oxidation numbers. *[1]*

(ii) Describe using a labelled diagram, the essential components of an electrolytic cell. *[3]*

(iii) Explain why solid sodium chloride does not conduct electricity but **molten** sodium chloride does. *[2]*

(iv) Molten sodium chloride undergoes electrolysis in an electrolytic cell. For each electrode deduce the half-equation and state whether oxidation or reduction takes place. Deduce the equation of the overall cell reaction including state symbols. *[5]*

(v) Electrolysis has made it possible to obtain reactive metals such as aluminium from their ores, which has resulted in significant developments in engineering and technology. State **one** reason why aluminium is preferred to iron in many uses. *[1]*

(vi) Outline **two** differences between an electrolytic cell and a voltaic cell. *[2]*

[Taken from paper 2, time zone 2, May 2009]

How do I approach the question?

(i)   You simply have to remember the definition.

(ii) You need to sketch a diagram showing the main parts (essential components) of the cell. Diagrams like these have to be clear but not artistic, and should always be labelled.

(iii) The explanation needs to be in terms of the movement of ions, not electrons.

(iv) The wording of the question makes it clear exactly what you have to write to score full marks—three equations (one including state symbols) and a statement of where oxidation and reduction occur.

(v)   You just need to state a relevant property.

(vi) You need to be aware of the two different types of cell and then clearly state two differences between them.

What are the key areas of the syllabus?

*   Redox definitions in terms of oxidation numbers and electron transfer
*   Electrolytic cell diagrams and equations
*   Comparison of electrolytic and voltaic cells

This answer achieved 5/14

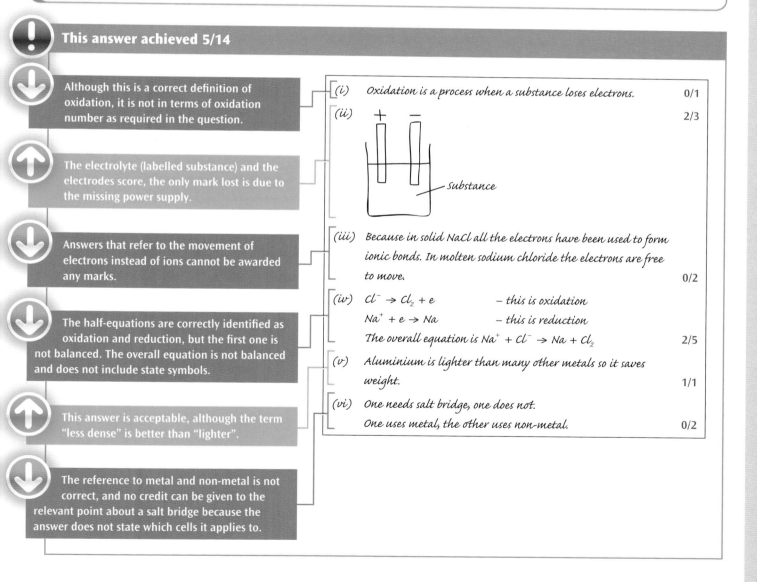

Although this is a correct definition of oxidation, it is not in terms of oxidation number as required in the question.

The electrolyte (labelled substance) and the electrodes score, the only mark lost is due to the missing power supply.

Answers that refer to the movement of electrons instead of ions cannot be awarded any marks.

The half-equations are correctly identified as oxidation and reduction, but the first one is not balanced. The overall equation is not balanced and does not include state symbols.

This answer is acceptable, although the term "less dense" is better than "lighter".

The reference to metal and non-metal is not correct, and no credit can be given to the relevant point about a salt bridge because the answer does not state which cells it applies to.

(i)   Oxidation is a process when a substance loses electrons.   0/1

(ii)   2/3

+   —

— Substance

(iii) Because in solid NaCl all the electrons have been used to form ionic bonds. In molten sodium chloride the electrons are free to move.   0/2

(iv) $Cl^- \rightarrow Cl_2 + e$ – this is oxidation
      $Na^+ + e \rightarrow Na$ – this is reduction
      The overall equation is $Na^+ + Cl^- \rightarrow Na + Cl_2$ 2/5

(v)   Aluminium is lighter than many other metals so it saves weight.   1/1

(vi) One needs salt bridge, one does not.
      One uses metal, the other uses non-metal.   0/2

This answer achieved 7/14

This is a correct definition—the key word is "increase".

The power supply and the correctly labelled electrodes score, but "solution" is not the correct term to describe a molten electrolyte.

Answers that refer to the movement of electrons instead of ions cannot be awarded any marks.

The first half-equation is correct, but the other two equations are not, and there is no reference to oxidation or reduction.

Although "less dense" is a better answer, "lighter" scored the mark.

There are five ways to score 2 marks. This answer scores for the ideas that an electrolytic cell needs electricity and for the correct electrodes at which oxidation and reduction occur.

(i) Oxidation is when an element goes from a low oxidation number to a high oxidation number, ie an increase in oxidation number.   1/1

(ii)   2/3

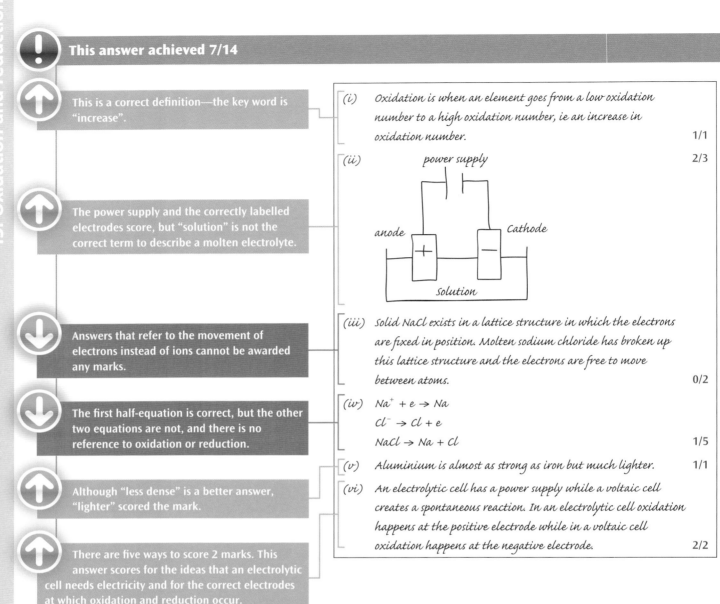

power supply

anode   Cathode

Solution

(iii) Solid NaCl exists in a lattice structure in which the electrons are fixed in position. Molten sodium chloride has broken up this lattice structure and the electrons are free to move between atoms.   0/2

(iv) $Na^+ + e \rightarrow Na$
$Cl^- \rightarrow Cl + e$
$NaCl \rightarrow Na + Cl$ 1/5

(v) Aluminium is almost as strong as iron but much lighter.   1/1

(vi) An electrolytic cell has a power supply while a voltaic cell creates a spontaneous reaction. In an electrolytic cell oxidation happens at the positive electrode while in a voltaic cell oxidation happens at the negative electrode.   2/2

This answer achieved 10/14

This is a correct definition, although "gain" is not really the right word, but "rise" is equivalent to "increase".

Although the diagram is not very neat, it shows the three features needed for full marks—the electrolyte, the electrodes and signs, and the power supply.

Answers that refer to the movement of electrons instead of ions cannot be awarded any marks.

All three equations are correct, except that the last one does not include state symbols.

Again, "lighter" was accepted.

There are five ways to score 2 marks. This answer scores for the first point about the spontaneous reaction. The second point is correct about the electrolytic cell, but not all electrodes in voltaic cells change into ions (the platinum electrode in the hydrogen half-cell does not), and "erode" (which suggests wearing away) is not a correct term.

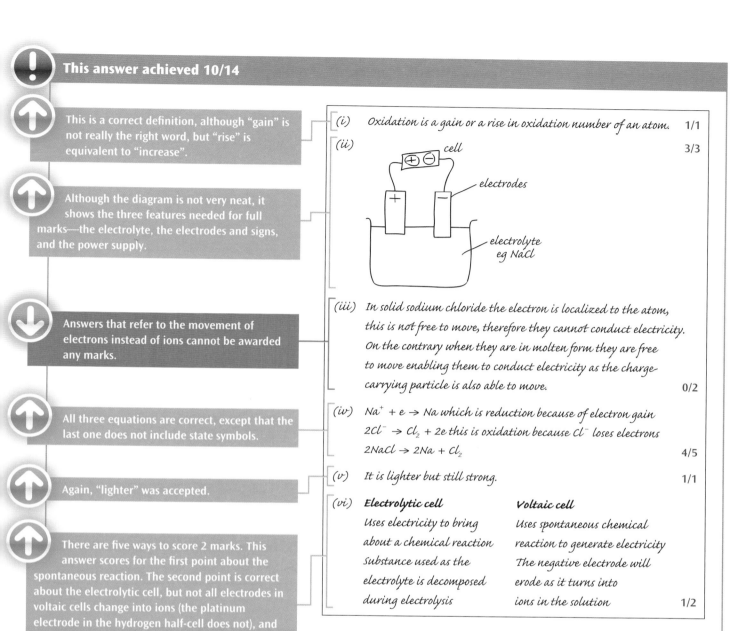

(i)   Oxidation is a gain or a rise in oxidation number of an atom.   1/1

(ii)   3/3

(iii)   In solid sodium chloride the electron is localized to the atom, this is not free to move, therefore they cannot conduct electricity. On the contrary when they are in molten form they are free to move enabling them to conduct electricity as the charge-carrying particle is also able to move.   0/2

(iv) $Na^+ + e \rightarrow Na$ which is reduction because of electron gain
        $2Cl^- \rightarrow Cl_2 + 2e$ this is oxidation because Cl^- loses electrons
        $2NaCl \rightarrow 2Na + Cl_2$ 4/5

(v)   It is lighter but still strong.   1/1

(vi)   **Electrolytic cell**   **Voltaic cell**

        Uses electricity to bring   Uses spontaneous chemical
        about a chemical reaction   reaction to generate electricity

        Substance used as the   The negative electrode will
        electrolyte is decomposed   erode as it turns into
        during electrolysis   ions in the solution   1/2

4. (a) Define oxidation in terms of electron transfer. *[1]*

    (b) Chlorine can be made by reacting concentrated hydrochloric acid with potassium manganate(VII), $KMnO_4$.

    $$2KMnO_4(aq) + 16HCl(aq) \rightarrow 2MnCl_2(aq) + 2KCl(aq) + 5Cl_2(aq) + 8H_2O(aq)$$

    (i) State the oxidation number of manganese in $KMnO_4$ and in $MnCl_2$.
    $KMnO_4$
    $MnCl_2$

    (ii) Deduce which species has been oxidized in this reaction and state the change in oxidation number that it has undergone. *[2]*

[Taken from paper 2, time zone 1, May 2009]

How do I approach the question?

(a) You just have to state the correct definition, remembering to refer to oxidation and not to reduction.

(b) (i) You have to apply the rules about oxidation number to the two compounds shown. Remember that oxidation numbers that are not part of a formula should consist of a sign and a number, for example +3 (but not just a number, for example, not just 3), or a Roman numeral in brackets, such as (III).

    (ii) After identifying the species, the best way to state the change in oxidation number is to give the initial and final oxidation numbers.

What are the key areas of the syllabus?

- Redox definitions in terms of electron transfer and changes in oxidation number

This answer achieved 0/5

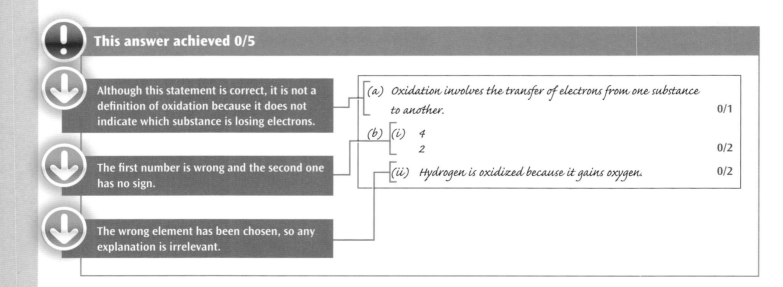

Although this statement is correct, it is not a definition of oxidation because it does not indicate which substance is losing electrons.

The first number is wrong and the second one has no sign.

The wrong element has been chosen, so any explanation is irrelevant.

(a) Oxidation involves the transfer of electrons from one substance to another. 0/1

(b) (i) 4
        2 0/2

(ii) Hydrogen is oxidized because it gains oxygen. 0/2

This answer achieved 3/5

Although the first part of the sentence is correct, the second part is a definition of reduction. As the student has not made it clear which definition is oxidation (they cannot both be correct), no mark can be awarded.

Although these are the correct oxidation numbers when included in the formulas, they are not shown in the correct way as required by the question—they are Roman numerals. However, as they are numerically correct, one mark has been awarded.

The right species has been chosen and both oxidation numbers are correct.

(a) Oxidation involves the loss of electrons by one substance and the gain of electrons by another substance.   0/1

(b) (i) (VII)
       (II)   1/2

(ii) Chlorine is oxidized because it goes from −1 to 0   2/2

This answer achieved 5/5

The idea of electron loss is clear in this answer.

Both are correct—note that Arabic numerals, not Roman ones, have been used and the necessary signs have been included.

The right species has been chosen and both oxidation numbers are correct. Note that there are two possible identities for the species. It is actually the Cl⁻ ion that is oxidized, but as the equation shows HCl, this is acceptable provided that the answer makes it clear that it is the Cl and not the H that is being oxidized.

(a) Oxidation involves the loss of electrons from one substance.   1/1

(b) (i) +7
       +2   2/2

(ii) HCl is oxidized because the oxidation number of Cl goes from −1 to 0.   2/2

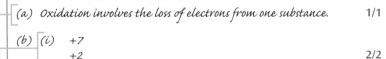

14. Organic chemistry

Introduction

You should know:

- two major features of a homologous series are that each member of the series differs from the previous one by CH_2, and they have the same functional group and thus similar chemical properties
- also they have the same general formula and their physical properties gradually change with increasing chain length as van der Waals' forces increase
- molecules with the same molecular formula such as C_4H_{10} may be arranged in space in different ways, for example $CH_3CH_2CH_2CH_3$ or $CH_3CH(CH_3)CH_3$, and these are called structural isomers
- how to use the IUPAC rules for naming compounds containing up to six carbon atoms
- the terms primary, secondary and tertiary to describe carbon atoms.

You should be able to:

- predict and explain the trends in the boiling points of members of a homologous series
- distinguish between the empirical formula, which is a ratio of elements, and the molecular formula, which gives the actual number of atoms of each element—for example, the molecular formula of butane is C_4H_{10} but its empirical formula is C_2H_5
- deduce the structural formula of the isomers of compounds containing up to six carbon atoms and the following functional groups: alcohol, aldehyde, ketone, carboxylic acid and halide
- relate the volatility (boiling point) and solubility in water to the structure of the organic molecule and the intermolecular forces holding the molecules together—for example, ethanol has an —OH functional group, which can hydrogen bond to water, making it soluble in water, and it can hydrogen bond to other alcohol molecules, giving it a relatively high boiling point.

Be prepared

- You must learn the following names and structures.

Name	Molecular formula	Structural formula	General formula
Methane	CH_4	CH_4	C_nH_{2n+2}
Ethane	C_2H_6	CH_3CH_3	C_nH_{2n+2}
Propane	C_3H_8	$CH_3CH_2CH_3$	C_nH_{2n+2}
Butane	C_4H_{10}	$CH_3(CH_2)_2CH_3$	C_nH_{2n+2}
Pentane	C_5H_{12}	$CH_3(CH_2)_3CH_3$	C_nH_{2n+2}
Hexane	C_6H_{14}	$CH_3(CH_2)_4CH_3$	C_nH_{2n+2}

- You must learn the following functional groups.

Name	Functional group formula	Example of formula	Example of name
Alcohol*	—OH	CH_3CH_2OH	ethanol
Aldehyde*	—CHO	CH_3CHO	ethanal
Ketone*	—CO	CH_3COCH_3	propanone
Carboxylic acid*	—COOH	CH_3COOH	ethanoic acid
Halide*	—Cl or —Br or —I or —F	CH_3CH_2Cl	chloroethane
Alkene*	—C=C—	CH_2CH_2	ethene
Amino	—NH_2	$CH_3CH_2NH_2$	ethylamine
Benzene ring	C_6H_6 or ⬡	$C_6H_5CH_3$	methylbenzene
Ester	—COO—	$HCOOCH_3$	methyl methanoate

- The examples given above are all based on molecules containing two or three carbon atoms. You must also be able to name those followed by a star (*).

Introduction (continued)

Example

(a) Which of the structures below is an aldehyde?

    A. CH_3CH_2CHO

    B. CH_3COCH_3

    C. CH_3CH_2COOH

    D. CH_3COOCH_3

The correct answer is A.

Aldehydes have CHO at the end of the molecule, so A is the correct answer. B is a ketone, C is a carboxylic acid and D is an ester.

(b) Which of the substances below is **most** soluble in water?

    A. $CH_2OHCHOHCH_2OH$

    B. CH_3COCH_3

    C. CH_3CH_2COOH

    D. CH_3COOCH_3

A is the most soluble.

Solubility depends on intermolecular forces, and molecules that have an OH group can hydrogen bond and so are more soluble in water. This means that A and C will be the most soluble. A has three OH groups and three carbon atoms. C has only one OH group but also three carbon atoms. So A is more soluble than C, as it can make the most hydrogen bonds, and they each have the same number of carbon atoms that cannot. So A is the most soluble.

(c) How many structural isomers are possible with the molecular formula C_6H_{14}?

    A.   4

    B.   5

    C.   6

    D.   7

Answer is B.

To answer this, you have to work out how many possible structures there are with a chain of six carbons (one: hexane), with a chain of five carbons (two: 2-methylpentane and 3-methylpentane) and with a chain of four carbons (two: 2,2-dimethylbutane and 2,3-dimethylbutane). This is a total of 5.

(d) Which statement about neighbouring members of all homologous series is correct?

    A.   They have the same empirical formula.

    B.   They differ by a CH_2 group.

    C.   They possess different functional groups.

    D.   They differ in their degree of unsaturation.

Correct answer is B.

This question is easily answered. They do not have the same empirical formula—only the same general formula. They possess the same functional groups and so therefore will have the same degree of unsaturation (as this depends on how many double carbon bonds they have). So the correct answer is B.

(e) What is the IUPAC name for $CH_3CH_2CH(CH_3)_2$?

    A.   1,1-dimethylpropane

    B.   2-methylbutane

    C.   isopentane

    D.   ethyldimethylmethane

B is the correct answer.

To answer this question correctly, you need to draw the structure so you can identify the longest carbon chain in the molecule. When you do that, you can see that the chain has four carbons, and a methyl group is attached to the second carbon, making B the correct answer.

Alkanes

You should know:

- alkanes are generally unreactive, because both the C—C and C—H bonds are strong and also non-polar

- alkanes have very similar electronegativities

- alkanes undergo combustion—they burn very exothermically in oxygen to produce carbon dioxide CO_2 and water H_2O (this is complete combustion), for example

$$CH_4(g) + 2O_2(g) \rightarrow CO_2(g) + 2H_2O(g)$$

or if the oxygen is limited they can produce poisonous carbon monoxide CO or soot C instead, for example

$$CH_4(g) + O_2(g) \rightarrow C(g) + 2H_2O(g)$$

- alkanes react with chlorine and bromine in the presence of ultraviolet light (sunlight) via a free-radical substitution reaction.

You should be able to:

- describe the free-radical substitution mechanism using the terms initiation, propagation and termination

- describe initiation in terms of homolytic fission, which leads to the formation of free radicals, which have the symbol ·.

Be prepared

- Be able to write equations for the complete and incomplete combustion of alkanes.

- Learn the following mechanism:
Initiation (in UV light)	$Cl_2 \rightarrow 2Cl\cdot$
Propagation	$CH_4 + Cl\cdot \rightarrow CH_3\cdot + HCl$
	$CH_3\cdot + Cl_2 \rightarrow CH_3Cl + Cl\cdot$
Termination	$Cl\cdot + Cl\cdot \rightarrow Cl_2$
or	$CH_3\cdot + CH_3\cdot \rightarrow C_2H_6$

Example

(a) Which of the following are characteristics typical of a free radical?

    I.   It has a lone pair of electrons.
    II. It can be formed by the homolytic fission of a covalent bond.
    III. It is uncharged.

A. I and II only

B. I and III only

C. II and III only

D. I, II and III

The correct answer is C.

Free radicals form when a bond splits homolytically, so the pair of electrons in the covalent bond are split between the two atoms making the bond and each then gains an unpaired electron. This makes the species very reactive. Since only one electron is gained by each atom, there is no net loss or gain of electrons, so the free radical is uncharged. So statement I is false and statements II and III are true, so the correct answer is C.

(b) Which statement is correct about the reaction between methane and chlorine?

A. It involves heterolytic fission and Cl^- ions.

B. It involves heterolytic fission and $Cl\cdot$ radicals.

C. It involves homolytic fission and Cl^- ions.

D. It involves homolytic fission and $Cl\cdot$ radicals.

D is correct.

Clearly since homolytic fission is involved and a free radical forms, the correct answer is D.

Alkenes

You should know:

- the general formula of alkenes is C_nH_{2n}

- alkenes are hydrocarbons containing a double carbon bond that makes them more reactive than alkanes

- alkenes undergo addition reactions with hydrogen, halogens, hydrogen halides and water

- alkenes (monomers) can join to each other by addition polymerization to give long chain molecules (polymers).

You should be able to:

- distinguish between alkenes and alkanes using bromine water—alkenes decolourize it and alkanes do not

- outline the polymerization of alkenes to form polyethene, polypropene and PVC (polychloroethene).

Be prepared

- Alkenes are very important as they form the basis of the plastics industry.

- Also, hydration of ethene forms ethanol industrially, and unsaturated fats are hydrogenated to make margarine.

Example

(a) Two reactions of an alkene, **B**, are shown below.

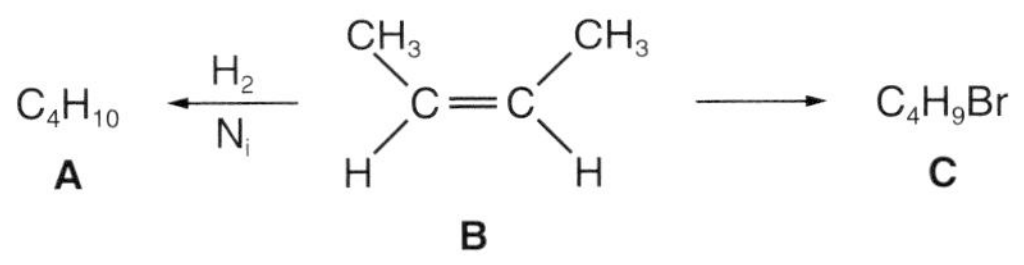

(i) State the name of **A** and write an equation for its complete combustion. Explain why the incomplete combustion of **A** is dangerous.

A is butane.

Butane A is produced from but-2-ene B. The equation for the complete combustion reaction is

$$C_4H_{10}(g) + \tfrac{13}{2}O_2(g) \rightarrow 4CO_2(g) + 5H_2O(l)$$

But to give whole-number coefficients every number is doubled.

$$2C_4H_{10}(g) + 13O_2(g) \rightarrow 8CO_2(g) + 10H_2O(l)$$

If the oxygen supply is limited, CO is produced:

$$2C_4H_{10}(g) + 9O_2(g) \rightarrow 8CO(g) + 10H_2O(g)$$

CO is poisonous because it combines with haemoglobin, and stops it carrying oxygen around the body.

(ii) Outline a test to distinguish between **A** and **B**, stating the result in each case.

You would add bromine water $Br_2(aq)$ to distinguish between the alkene B and the alkane A—the alkane A would have no effect but the alkene B would decolourize the $Br_2(aq)$, and its colour would change from orange to colourless.

(iii) Write an equation for the conversion of **B** to **C**. State the type of reaction taking place and draw the structure of **C**.

$$CH_3CH{=}CHCH_3 + HBr \rightarrow CH_3CHBrCH_2CH_3$$

This is an example of an addition reaction, and the H and Br add across the double bond.

(b) $H_2C{=}CH_2$ can react to form a polymer. Name this **type** of polymer and draw the structural formula of a section of this polymer consisting of three repeating units.

This is an example of addition polymerization.

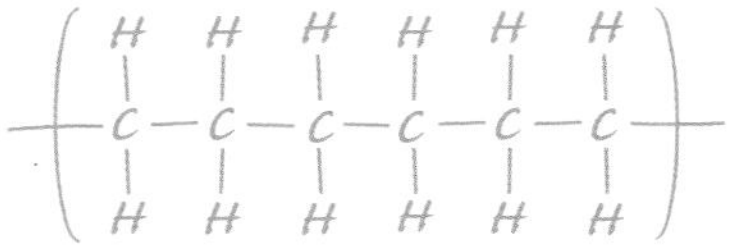

A chain with three units will contain six carbon atoms. These are all now joined by single bonds. Here the continuation bonds are very important for the mark, as the chain keeps going, and the brackets are also advisable.

Alcohols

You should know:

- all alcohols contain the OH functional group and so can hydrogen bond with water and each other

- alcohols will combust in oxygen and are good fuels

- alcohols can undergo oxidation if they are reacted with acidified potassium dichromate(VI).

You should be able to:

- write equations for the combustion of alcohols

- describe the conditions needed during oxidation to produce an aldehyde (by distilling off the product as it forms) and a carboxylic acid (by heating the alcohol under reflux).

Be prepared

- Primary alcohols are oxidized to aldehydes and then to carboxylic acids.

- Secondary alcohols are oxidized to ketones.

- Tertiary alcohols cannot be oxidized.

Example

Propene can be converted to propanoic acid in three steps:

$$propene \xrightarrow{step\ 1} propan\text{-}1\text{-}ol \xrightarrow{step\ 2} propanal \xrightarrow{step\ 3} propanoic\ acid$$

State the type of reaction occurring in steps 2 and 3 and the reagents needed. Describe how the conditions of the reaction can be altered to obtain the maximum amount of propanal, and, in a separate experiment, to obtain the maximum amount of propanoic acid.

This is an oxidation or redox reaction, as the oxidation number of the carbon has increased. To perform the oxidation, you need a strong oxidizing agent such as potassium dichromate(VI) $K_2Cr_2O_7$ with sulfuric acid. To get propanal you must distill off the propanal as it is formed. To get propanoic acid you need to heat under reflux.

Heating under reflux means that you are heating the liquid without allowing the vapour to escape—the vapour is cooled as it forms and returned to the heating vessel.

Halogenoalkanes

You should know:

- that halogenoalkanes react with sodium hydroxide to produce alcohols
- S_N1 is nucleophilic substitution—unimolecular, and S_N2 is nucleophilic substitution—bimolecular.

You should be able to:

- explain the process of nucleophilic substitution with equations and mechanisms
- show that S_N1 occurs with tertiary halogenoalkanes and S_N2 occurs with primary halogenoalkanes—secondary halogenoalkanes can react with both mechanisms.

Be prepared

- You must be able to draw the mechanisms for S_N1 and S_N2 using curly arrows to show the movement of pairs of electrons, as shown below.

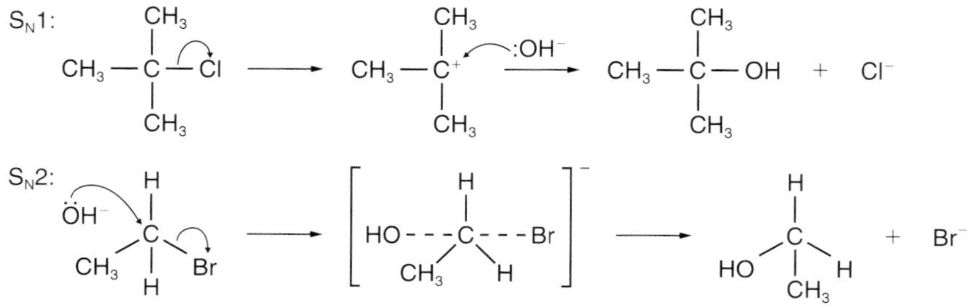

- During nucleophilic substitution, heterolytic fission occurs, because when a bond breaks both the electrons in a covalent bond are transferred to one atom.

Halogenoalkanes (continued)

Example

The following transition state is formed during the reaction of a halogenoalkane with aqueous sodium hydroxide:

$$\left[\begin{array}{c} H_3C \qquad CH_3 \\ HO ---C--- Br \\ H \end{array} \right]^-$$

(a) Deduce the structure of the halogenoalkane. Classify it as primary, secondary or tertiary, giving a reason for your choice.

If we take away the attacking nucleophile, OH^-, the formula of the halogenoalkane is $(CH_3)_2CHBr$. It is a secondary halogenoalkane as the carbon attached to bromine is attached to two alkyl groups.

(b) The mechanism of this reaction is described as S_N2. Explain what is meant by the symbols in S_N2. Predict a rate expression for this reaction.

The symbols mean nucleophilic substitution which is bimolecular. There is a molecularity of two as there are two species in the rate-determining step. For this reason the rate expression contains both the halogenoalkane and the nucleophile, OH^-, and can be described as:

$$rate = k\,[(CH_3)_2CHBr][OH^-]$$

(c) The same halogenoalkane reacts with sodium hydroxide by an S_N1 mechanism. Deduce the structure of the intermediate formed in this reaction.

When this is the case, the bromine leaves as Br^- and leaves behind a carbocation whose formula is $(CH_3)_2CH^+$.

As this is a secondary halogenoalkane, it can react via S_N1 as well as S_N2.

Reaction pathways

You should know:

• the pathways in the following diagram.

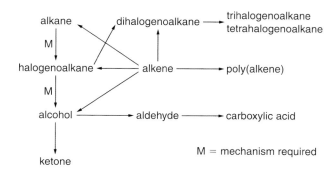

M = mechanism required

You should be able to:

• suggest how to form a compound in one or two steps if given a starting product.

Example

(a) Suggest how but-2-ene could be converted to butanone in two steps. Include the reagents and conditions needed and write equations to describe each step.

You first react but-2-ene with steam in the presence of a catalyst:

$$CH_3CHCHCH_3 + H_2O \rightarrow CH_3CH(OH)CH_2CH_3$$

Then you oxidize the butan-2-ol formed to butanone by heating with acidified potassium dichromate(VI), put simply as

$$CH_3CHOHCH_2CH_3 + [O] \rightarrow CH_3COCH_2CH_3 + H_2O$$

Alkenes react by addition reactions and you convert an alkene to an alcohol by adding H_2O. If you then have a secondary alcohol, it can be oxidized to a ketone. The full equation for the second reaction is

$$3CH_3CH(OH)CH_2CH_3 + Cr_2O_7^{2-} + 8H^+ \rightarrow$$
$$3CH_3COCH_2CH_3 + 7H_2O + 2Cr^{3+}$$

(b) Suggest how methane could be converted to methanol in two steps. Include the reagents and conditions needed and write equations to describe each step.

To convert an alkane to an alcohol, you need to first make a halogenoalkane. To synthesize a halogenoalkane, you need to put methane with chlorine in the presence of UV light. This will lead to a free-radical substitution reaction and one of the products will be chloromethane. By reacting 1 mol of methane with 1 mol of chlorine you are more likely to get chloromethane rather than dichloro-, trichloro- or tetrachloromethane. Once you have chloromethane, you can convert it to an alcohol by heating with aqueous

sodium hydroxide and it will form an alcohol via an S_N2 mechanism. So equations and reagents are:

Step 1, conditions—UV light

$$CH_4 + Cl_2 \rightarrow CH_3Cl + HCl$$

Step 2, conditions—heat with NaOH(aq)

$$CH_3Cl + NaOH \rightarrow CH_3OH + NaCl$$

7. (a) Three compounds with similar relative molecular masses are butane, propanal and propan-1-ol.

    (i)   List the three compounds in order of increasing boiling point (lowest first) and explain the differences in their boiling points. [4]

    (ii) Predict, with an explanation, which of the three compounds is **least** soluble or miscible in water. [2]

    (iii) When propan-1-ol is oxidized using a warm acidified solution of potassium dichromate(VI) two different organic products can be obtained. Deduce the name and structural formula for each of these two products. [3]

    (iv) Propan-2-ol is an isomer of propan-1-ol. Draw the structure of propan-2-ol. [1]

    (v)   Identify the class of alcohols that propan-2-ol belongs to and state the name of the organic product formed when it is oxidized by an acidified solution of potassium dichromate(VI). [2]

    (b) Ethanol can be formed from ethene in a two step reaction:

    (i)   State the name of the reagent used for step 1. [1]

    (ii) State the name of the reagent and the conditions used for step 2. [2]

    (iii) The mechanism involved in step 2 is S_N2. Explain how the reaction proceeds using curly arrows to represent the movement of electron pairs. [3]

    (iv) Outline how ethanol is manufactured from ethene in industry and state **one** important commercial use of ethanol. [2]

[Taken from paper 2, time zone 1, May 2009]

How do I approach the question?

(a) (i)   You need to consider the structure of each compound, then deduce the strongest type of intermolecular forces present.

(ii)   You need to remember that molecules with the greatest solubility in water are those that have polar bonds and can form dipole–dipole attractions (or, even better, hydrogen bonds).

(iii)   You need to remember the different ways in which alcohols can be oxidized, and that primary alcohols can be oxidized to either aldehydes or carboxylic acids, depending on the conditions.

(iv)   When the question states **draw the structure**, the minimum acceptable answer is a condensed structural formula, although it is safer to draw a displayed formula because there is less chance of making a mistake such as showing carbon atoms with three or five bonds.

(v)   You need to apply what you did in part (a)(iii).

(b) (i) and (ii)   You are being tested on reaction pathways—the reagents needed to convert one organic compound to another. Remember that if a name is asked for, then a formula will not do (and the other way round).

(iii)   You need to draw the mechanism very carefully because what might seem to be small differences between what you find in a textbook and what you draw could mean the difference between full marks and no marks. In particular, be careful about where the curly arrows start from and point to, and if there is a transition state with five bonds around a carbon atom, then two of them should be shown as dashed lines.

(iv)   Two brief statements are needed.

What are the key areas of the syllabus?

- Names, structural formulas of organic compounds
- The oxidation of alcohols
- Reaction mechanisms, in this case S_N2

This answer achieved 6/20

The order is correct and the explanation for propan-1-ol also scores.

Butane is correctly identified, but the explanation is not correct.

Although one compound is correctly identified, both are needed for a mark. The formula given is for butanoic acid, not propanoic acid, and in any case it is not a structural formula.

The structure has been clearly drawn—note that a condensed formula like CH₃CH(OH)CH₃ would have been accepted. It is often easier to draw the structures with all or most of the atoms shown separately because it is then easier to check that all the carbon atoms have the correct valency.

The class of alcohol has not been stated and ketone is the name of the homologous series, but the specific compound name propanone is needed for the mark.

This is the correct name—note that a formula would not have been accepted.

This answer shows no understanding of reaction mechanisms.

(a) (i) butane, propanal, propan-1-ol
Butane has the weakest intermolecular forces. Propan-1-ol has hydrogen bonding. 2/4

(ii) Butane is the least soluble since it has no polar bonds. 1/2

(iii) C_3H_7COOH propanoic acid. 0/3

(iv)
$$H-\overset{\overset{\displaystyle H}{|}}{\underset{\underset{\displaystyle H}{|}}{C}}-\overset{\overset{\displaystyle H}{|}}{\underset{\underset{\displaystyle OH}{|}}{C}}-\overset{\overset{\displaystyle H}{|}}{\underset{\underset{\displaystyle H}{|}}{C}}-H$$
1/1

(v) ketone 0/2

(b) (i) hydrogen bromide 1/1

(ii) NaOH 0/2

(iii)
$$CH_3-\overset{\overset{\displaystyle Br}{|}}{\underset{\underset{\displaystyle H}{|}}{C}}-H \longrightarrow CH_3-\overset{\overset{\displaystyle NaBr}{|}}{\underset{\underset{\displaystyle OH}{|}}{C}}-H$$
NaOH
0/3

(iv) Ethanol is manufactured from ethane. It can be used in cars instead of gasoline. 1/2

Although there is no indication of how ethanol is manufactured, a mark is awarded for a correct use.

This answer achieved 11/20

The order is correct, and all three types of intermolecular force have been given for the right compounds.

Butane is correctly identified, but the explanation is incomplete—there is nothing about why the two molecules do not interact.

Both compounds are correctly identified by name and formula.

A correct structure is clearly drawn.

The product has been correctly identified.

The question asked for the name, so the mark cannot be awarded.

Ideally the curly arrow should come from a lone pair of electrons on the oxygen atom, but coming from the negative charge is accepted in this case. It must not be shown coming from the hydrogen atom. The transition state and the breaking of the C—Br bond have not been shown, so no further marks are awarded.

There is no mention of the manufacture of ethene and although ethanol is present in alcoholic drinks, it is not made from ethene in this use.

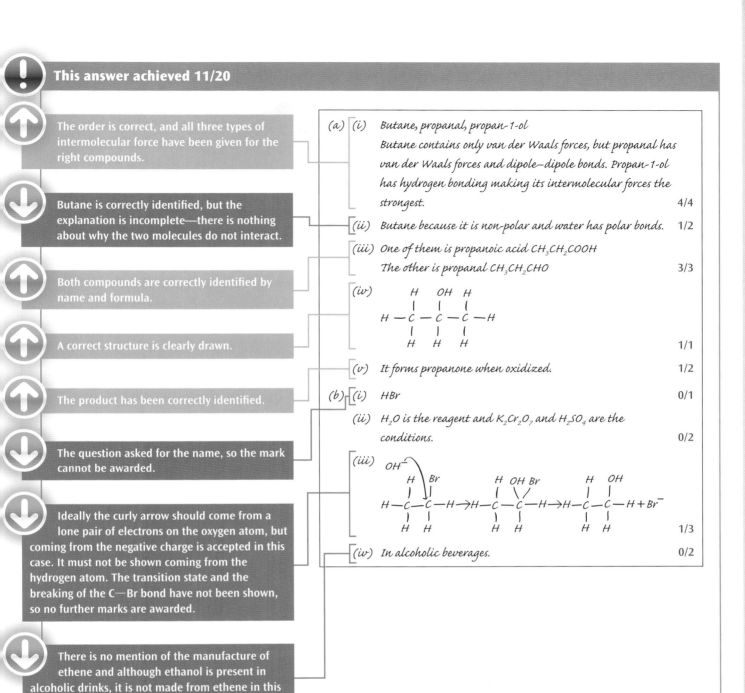

(a) (i) Butane, propanal, propan-1-ol
Butane contains only van der Waals forces, but propanal has van der Waals forces and dipole–dipole bonds. Propan-1-ol has hydrogen bonding making its intermolecular forces the strongest. 4/4

(ii) Butane because it is non-polar and water has polar bonds. 1/2

(iii) One of them is propanoic acid CH_3CH_2COOH
The other is propanal CH_3CH_2CHO 3/3

(iv)

$$H-\underset{\underset{H}{|}}{\overset{\overset{H}{|}}{C}}-\underset{\underset{H}{|}}{\overset{\overset{OH}{|}}{C}}-\underset{\underset{H}{|}}{\overset{\overset{H}{|}}{C}}-H$$

1/1

(v) It forms propanone when oxidized. 1/2

(b) (i) HBr 0/1

(ii) H_2O is the reagent and $K_2Cr_2O_7$ and H_2SO_4 are the conditions. 0/2

(iii)

1/3

(iv) In alcoholic beverages. 0/2

This answer achieved 16/20

The order is correct, and all three types of intermolecular force have been given for the right compounds. Note that although "van der Waals' forces" is the commonest name used for the weakest of these, other names, such as "London" and "dispersion" forces are acceptable.

The comparison of polarities and the inability to form hydrogen bonds each scores a mark.

A correct structure is given.

Both the class of alcohol and the name of the product formed are correct.

The name scores the mark here—the formula is ignored.

The only mark awarded is for correctly showing the breaking of the C—Br bond. The curly arrow from OH⁻ should point to the C atom and not to the C—H bond. Although the transition state has square brackets and an overall negative charge, the C—Br and C—OH bonds should be partial bonds and shown as dashed or dotted lines, ideally at 180° to each other.

The mention of "ethene" and "steam" are enough to score the mark for the outline of the manufacture, and the use is correct.

(a) (i) *Butane, propanal, propan-1-ol*
Butane is non-polar with only weak London dispersion forces, so it has a low boiling point. Propanal has dipole–dipole bonds, so it has stronger intermolecular forces and has a higher boiling point. Propan-1-ol has dipole–dipole forces and hydrogen bonding as well, making its BP the highest due to its strong intermolecular forces.   4/4

(ii) *Butane because it is non-polar while water is polar, and therefore will not dissolve because like dissolves like.*
It cannot form hydrogen bonds with water molecules.   2/2

(iii) *Propanal*

$$H - \overset{\overset{\displaystyle H}{|}}{\underset{\underset{\displaystyle H}{|}}{C}} - \overset{\overset{\displaystyle H}{|}}{\underset{\underset{\displaystyle H}{|}}{C}} - \overset{\overset{\displaystyle H}{|}}{C} = O$$

Propanoic acid

$$H - \overset{\overset{\displaystyle H}{|}}{\underset{\underset{\displaystyle H}{|}}{C}} - \overset{\overset{\displaystyle H}{|}}{\underset{\underset{\displaystyle H}{|}}{C}} - \overset{\overset{\displaystyle OH}{|}}{C} = O$$
    3/3

(iv)
$$H - \overset{\overset{\displaystyle H}{|}}{\underset{\underset{\displaystyle H}{|}}{C}} - \overset{\overset{\displaystyle OH}{|}}{\underset{\underset{\displaystyle H}{|}}{C}} - \overset{\overset{\displaystyle H}{|}}{\underset{\underset{\displaystyle H}{|}}{C}} - H$$
    1/1

(v) *Secondary alcohols. Forms a ketone when oxidized, in this case propanone.*   2/2

(b) (i) *HBr, hydrobromic acid.*   1/1

(ii) *H₂O water, acidic conditions with H₂SO₄*   0/2

(iii)

$$H - \overset{\overset{\displaystyle H}{|}}{\underset{\underset{\displaystyle H}{|}}{C}} - \overset{\overset{\displaystyle Br}{|}}{\underset{\underset{\displaystyle H}{|}}{C}} - H \quad OH^- \longrightarrow \left[H - \overset{\overset{\displaystyle H}{|}}{\underset{\underset{\displaystyle H}{|}}{C}} - \overset{\overset{\displaystyle Br}{|}}{\underset{\underset{\displaystyle H}{|}}{C}} \overset{OH}{\underset{H}{\big<}} \right]^- \longrightarrow H - \overset{\overset{\displaystyle H}{|}}{\underset{\underset{\displaystyle H}{|}}{C}} - \overset{\overset{\displaystyle OH}{|}}{\underset{\underset{\displaystyle H}{|}}{C}} - H + Br^-$$
    1/3

(iv) *Ethanol is manufactured by exposing ethene to warm steam, which converts ethene into ethanol. Ethanol could be used for fuel.*   2/2

15. Measurement and data processing

Much of the content of this topic is covered throughout the rest of the book. However, we have included those topics here that have not been covered.

Uncertainty and error in measurement and calculated results

You should know:

- the difference between a random error, such as reading the scale on a thermometer, and a systematic error, such as heat loss in an energetics experiment
- random uncertainties can be reduced by repeating an experiment exactly and averaging the results obtained.

You should be able to:

- distinguish between precision, where repeated readings are very close to each other, and accuracy, where a value is close to the true value
- state the uncertainty range associated with a random error—for example, if a burette measures to $0.10\,cm^3$, the uncertainty range will be $\pm0.05\,cm^3$
- state an answer to the correct number of significant figures
- calculate and state absolute and percentage errors.

Example

The following diagram shows a set of experimental data points, X, determined when one experimental measurement was repeated three times. The centre of the diagram represents the ideal value calculated from theory. What statement is correct about these measurements?

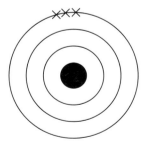

A. The measurements involve low accuracy and low precision.
B. The measurements involve low accuracy and high precision.
C. The measurements involve high accuracy and low precision.
D. The measurements involve high accuracy and high precision.

The answer is B.

The answer here is B because the crosses are close together, suggesting high precision. However, they are all far away from the central target, suggesting low accuracy.

We hope that you have enjoyed the book and that you will continue to use it throughout the year to help you to prepare for your exams.

Finally, we have added a set of past exam papers from May 2010 to which you may apply your new skills. You can either take these under exam conditions or refer back to the book, the choice is yours.

Paper 1

1. What is the coefficient of Fe_3O_4 when the following equation is balanced using the lowest whole numbers?

$$\_\_ Al(s) + \_\_ Fe_3O_4(s) \rightarrow \_\_ Al_2O_3(s) + \_\_ Fe(s)$$

    A.   2

    B.   3

    C.   4

    D.   5

2. What is the mass, in g, of one molecule of ethane, C_2H_6?

    A. 3.0×10^{-23}

    B. 5.0×10^{-23}

    C.   30

    D. 1.8×10^{25}

3. Which molecular formula is also an empirical formula?

    A. PCl_3

    B. C_2H_4

    C. H_2O_2

    D. $C_6H_{12}O_6$

4. Which of the following is consistent with Avogadro's law?

A. $\dfrac{P}{T}$ = constant (V, n constant)

B. $\dfrac{V}{T}$ = constant (P, n constant)

C. Vn = constant (P, T constant)

D. $\dfrac{V}{n}$ = constant (P, T constant)

5. A sample of element X contains 69 % of ^{63}X and 31 % of ^{65}X. What is the relative atomic mass of X in this sample?

A. 63.0

B. 63.6

C. 65.0

D. 69.0

6. How many electrons does the ion $^{31}_{15}P^{3-}$ contain?

A. 12

B. 15

C. 16

D. 18

7. What is the electron arrangement of the Mg^{2+} ion?

A. 2,2

B. 2,8

C. 2,8,2

D. 2,8,8

8. Which property **decreases** down group 7 in the periodic table?

A. Melting point

B. Electronegativity

C. Atomic radius

D. Ionic radius

9. Which oxides produce an acidic solution when added to water?

    I. P_4O_{10}

    II. MgO

    III. SO_3

    A.   I and II only

    B.   I and III only

    C.   II and III only

    D.   I, II and III

10. What is the formula of magnesium fluoride?

    A. Mg_2F_3

    B. Mg_2F

    C. Mg_3F_2

    D. MgF_2

11. What is the shape of the ammonia molecule, NH_3?

    A.   Trigonal planar

    B.   Trigonal pyramidal

    C.   Linear

    D.   V-shaped (bent)

12. Which molecule is polar?

    A. CH_2Cl_2

    B. BCl_3

    C. Cl_2

    D. CCl_4

13. Which substance can form intermolecular hydrogen bonds in the liquid state?

    A. CH_3OCH_3

    B. CH_3CH_2OH

    C. CH_3CHO

    D. $CH_3CH_2CH_3$

14. Which compound has a covalent macromolecular (giant covalent) structure?

    A. $MgO(s)$

    B. $Al_2O_3(s)$

    C. $P_4O_{10}(s)$

    D. $SiO_2(s)$

15. The standard enthalpy changes for the combustion of carbon and carbon monoxide are shown below.

    $$C(s) + O_2(g) \rightarrow CO_2(g) \qquad \Delta H_c^{\ominus} = -394 \text{ kJ mol}^{-1}$$
    $$CO(g) + \tfrac{1}{2}O_2(g) \rightarrow CO_2(g) \qquad \Delta H_c^{\ominus} = -283 \text{ kJ mol}^{-1}$$

    What is the standard enthalpy change, in kJ, for the following reaction?

    $$C(s) + \tfrac{1}{2}O_2(g) \rightarrow CO(g)$$

    A.   −677

    B.   −111

    C.   +111

    D.   +677

16. Which is correct about energy changes during bond breaking and bond formation?

	Bond breaking	Bond formation
A.	exothermic and ΔH positive	endothermic and ΔH negative
B.	exothermic and ΔH negative	endothermic and ΔH positive
C.	endothermic and ΔH positive	exothermic and ΔH negative
D.	endothermic and ΔH negative	exothermic and ΔH positive

17. Which processes are exothermic?

    I.   Ice melting

    II.   Neutralization

    III.   Combustion

A.   I and II only

B.   I and III only

C.   II and III only

D.   I, II and III

18. Which unit could be used for the rate of a chemical reaction?

A.   mol

B. $mol\,dm^{-3}$

C. $mol\,dm^{-3}\,s^{-1}$

D. dm^{3}

19. Which of the following can **increase** the rate of a chemical reaction?

    I. Increasing the temperature

    II. Adding a catalyst

    III. Increasing the concentration of reactants

A. I and II only

B. I and III only

C. II and III only

D. I, II and III

20. What is the equilibrium constant expression, K_c, for the following reaction?

$$N_2O_4(g) \rightleftharpoons 2NO_2(g)$$

A. $K_c = \dfrac{[NO_2]}{[N_2O_4]}$

B. $K_c = \dfrac{[NO_2]^2}{[N_2O_4]}$

C. $K_c = \dfrac{[NO_2]}{[N_2O_4]^2}$

D. $K_c = [NO_2][N_2O_4]^2$

21. Consider the endothermic reaction below.

$$5CO(g) + I_2O_5(g) \rightleftharpoons 5CO_2(g) + I_2(g)$$

According to Le Chatelier's principle, which change would result in an increase in the amount of CO_2?

A. Increasing the temperature

B. Decreasing the temperature

C. Increasing the pressure

D. Decreasing the pressure

22. Which species behave as Brønsted-Lowry acids in the following reversible reaction?

$$H_2PO_4^-(aq) + CN^-(aq) \rightleftharpoons HCN(aq) + HPO_4^{2-}(aq)$$

A. HCN and CN^-

B. HCN and HPO_4^{2-}

C. $H_2PO_4^-$ and HPO_4^{2-}

D. HCN and $H_2PO_4^-$

23. Which of the following are weak acids in aqueous solution?

    I. CH_3COOH

    II. H_2CO_3

    III. HCl

A. I and II only

B. I and III only

C. II and III only

D. I, II and III

23. Which of the following are weak acids in aqueous solution?

    I. CH_3COOH

    II. H_2CO_3

    III. HCl

A. I and II only

B. I and III only

C. II and III only

D. I, II and III

25. What is the reducing agent in the reaction below?

$$2MnO_4^-(aq) + Br^-(aq) + H_2O(l) \rightarrow 2MnO_2(s) + BrO_3^-(aq) + 2OH^-(aq)$$

A. Br^-

B. BrO_3^-

C. MnO_4^-

D. MnO_2

26. Which changes could take place at the positive electrode (cathode) in a voltaic cell?

   I. $Zn^{2+}(aq)$ to $Zn(s)$

   II. $Cl_2(g)$ to $Cl^-(aq)$

   III. $Mg(s)$ to $Mg^{2+}(aq)$

A. I and II only

B. I and III only

C. II and III only

D. I, II and III

27. What is the structural formula of 2,3-dibromo-3-methylhexane?

A. $CH_3CHBrCHBrCH(CH_3)CH_2CH_3$

B. $CH_3CHBrCBr(CH_3)CH_2CH_2CH_3$

C. $CH_3CH_2CHBrCBr(CH_2CH_3)_2$

D. $CH_3CHBrCHBrCH(CH_2CH_3)_2$

28. What happens when a few drops of bromine water are added to excess hex-1-ene and the mixture is shaken?

    I.   The colour of the bromine water disappears.

    II.   The organic product formed does not contain any carbon-carbon double bonds.

    III.   2-bromohexane is formed.

    A.   I and II only

    B.   I and III only

    C.   II and III only

    D.   I, II and III

29. What is the product of the following reaction?

$$CH_3CH(OH)CH_3 \xrightarrow{Cr_2O_7^{2-}/H^+}$$

    A. CH_3COOH

    B. CH_3COCH_3

    C. CH_3CH_2COOH

    D. $CH_3CH_2CH_3$

30. How many significant figures are there in 0.00370?

    A.   2

    B.   3

    C.   5

    D.   6

Paper 2

Section A

1. The percentage by mass of calcium carbonate in eggshell was determined by adding excess hydrochloric acid to ensure that all the calcium carbonate had reacted. The excess acid left was then titrated with aqueous sodium hydroxide.

(a) A student added 27.20 cm³ of 0.200 mol dm⁻³ HCl to 0.188 g of eggshell. Calculate the amount, in mol, of HCl added. *[1]*

(b) The excess acid requires 23.80 cm³ of 0.100 mol dm⁻³ NaOH for neutralization. Calculate the amount, in mol, of acid that is in excess. *[1]*

(c) Determine the amount, in mol, of HCl that reacted with the calcium carbonate in the eggshell. *[1]*

(d) State the equation for the reaction of HCl with the calcium carbonate in the eggshell. *[2]*

(e) Determine the amount, in mol, of calcium carbonate in the sample of the eggshell. *[2]*

(f) Calculate the mass **and** the percentage by mass of calcium carbonate in the eggshell sample. *[3]*

(g) Deduce **one** assumption made in arriving at the percentage of calcium carbonate in the eggshell sample. *[1]*

2. Draw and label an energy level diagram for the hydrogen atom. In your diagram show how the series of lines in the ultraviolet and visible regions of its emission spectrum are produced, clearly labelling each series. *[4]*

3. Consider the bonding and structure of the period 3 elements.

(a) Explain the increase in the melting point from sodium to aluminium. *[2]*

(b) Explain why sulfur, S_8, has a higher melting point than phosphorus, P_4. *[2]*

(c) Explain why silicon has the highest melting point and argon has the lowest melting point. *[2]*

4. One important property of a rocket fuel mixture is the large volume of gaseous products formed which provide thrust. Hydrazine, N_2H_4, is often used as a rocket fuel. The combustion of hydrazine is represented by the equation below.

$$N_2H_4(g) + O_2(g) \rightarrow N_2(g) + 2H_2O(g) \qquad \Delta H_c^\ominus = -585 \, kJ \, mol^{-1}$$

(a) Hydrazine reacts with fluorine to produce nitrogen and hydrogen fluoride, all in the gaseous state. State an equation for the reaction. *[2]*

(b) Draw the Lewis structures for hydrazine and nitrogen. *[2]*

(c) Use the average bond enthalpies given in Table 10 of the Data Booklet to determine the enthalpy change for the reaction in part (a) above. *[3]*

(d) Based on your answers to parts (a) and (c), suggest whether a mixture of hydrazine and fluorine is a better rocket fuel than a mixture of hydrazine and oxygen. *[2]*

Section B

5. The periodic table shows the relationship between electron arrangement and the properties of elements and is a valuable tool for making predictions in chemistry.

(a) (i) Identify the property used to arrange the elements in the periodic table. *[1]*

   (ii) Outline **two** reasons why electronegativity increases across period 3 in the periodic table and **one** reason why noble gases are not assigned electronegativity values. *[3]*

(b) (i) Define the term *first ionization energy* of an atom. *[2]*

   (ii) Explain the general increasing trend in the first ionization energies of the period 3 elements, Na to Ar. *[2]*

   (iii) Explain why sodium conducts electricity but phosphorus does not. *[2]*

(c) The word *redox* comes from a combination of the terms *reduction* and *oxidation*. Redox reactions affect our daily lives.

   The overall reaction that takes place in a voltaic cell is shown below.

   $$Pb(s) + PbO_2(s) + 2H_2SO_4(aq) \rightarrow 2PbSO_4(s) + 2H_2O(l)$$

   (i) Determine the oxidation number of lead in Pb, PbO_2 and $PbSO_4$. *[1]*

   (ii) Deduce the oxidation and reduction half-equations taking place at the negative lead electrode (anode) and the positive lead(IV) oxide electrode (cathode). Deduce the oxidizing and reducing agents and state the direction of the electron flow between the electrodes. *[4]*

   (iii) In order to determine the position of three metals in a reactivity series, the metals were placed in different solutions of metal ions. The table below summarizes whether or not a reaction occurred.

	$Ag^+(aq)$	$Cu^{2+}(aq)$	$Pb^{2+}(aq)$
Ag(s)		No reaction	No reaction
Cu(s)	Reaction		No reaction
Pb(s)	Reaction	Reaction	

   State the equations for the **three** reactions that take place. Use this information to place the metals Ag, Cu and Pb in a reactivity series, with the strongest reducing agent first, and explain your reasoning. *[5]*

6. (a) Water is an important substance that is abundant on the Earth's surface. Water dissociates according to the following equation.

$$H_2O(l) \rightleftharpoons H^+(aq) + OH^-(aq)$$

    (i) State the equilibrium constant expression for the dissociation of water. *[1]*

    (ii) Explain why even a very acidic aqueous solution still has some OH^- ions present in it. *[1]*

    (iii) State and explain the effect of increasing temperature on the equilibrium constant above given that the dissociation of water is an endothermic process. *[3]*

    (iv) The pH of a solution is 2. If its pH is increased to 6, deduce how the hydrogen ion concentration changes. *[2]*

(b) In carbonated drinks containing dissolved carbon dioxide under high pressure, the following dynamic equilibrium exists.

$$CO_2(aq) \rightleftharpoons CO_2(g)$$

Describe the effect of opening a carbonated drink container and outline how this equilibrium is affected. *[2]*

(c) The graph below shows how the volume of carbon dioxide formed varies with time when a hydrochloric acid solution is added to **excess** calcium carbonate in a flask.

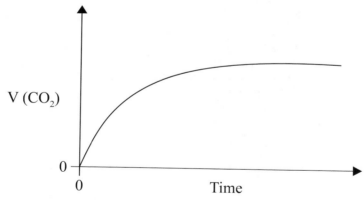

    (i) Explain the shape of the curve. *[3]*

    (ii) Copy the above graph on your answer sheet and sketch the curve you would obtain if **double** the volume of hydrochloric acid solution of **half** the concentration as in the example above is used instead, with all other variables kept constant from the original. Explain why the shape of the curve is different. *[4]*

    (iii) Outline **one** other way in which the rate of this reaction can be studied in a school laboratory. Sketch a graph to illustrate how the selected variable would change with time. *[2]*

    (iv) Define the term *activation energy* and state **one** reason why the reaction between calcium carbonate and hydrochloric acid takes place at a reasonably fast rate at room temperature. *[2]*

7. (a) Alkenes are an economically and chemically important family of organic compounds.

   (i) The reaction of alkenes with bromine water provides a test for unsaturation in the laboratory. Describe the colour change when bromine water is added to chloroethene. [1]

   (ii) Deduce the Lewis structure of chloroethene and identify the formula of the repeating unit of the polymer poly(chloroethene). [2]

   (iii) Besides polymerization, state **two** commercial uses of the reactions of alkenes. [2]

(b) But-2-ene can be converted to butan-2-one in **two** stages.

   (i) Draw the structural formulas of but-2-ene and butan-2-one. [2]

   (ii) Deduce a reaction pathway for the **two** stages of the reaction. Your answer should include the fully balanced equation for each stage of the reaction **and** the reagents and conditions for the two stages. [5]

(c) (i) Deduce the structural formulas of the **two** alcohol isomers of molecular formula C_3H_8O. Name each isomer and identify each as either a primary or a secondary alcohol. [3]

   (ii) Oxidation of the alcohol isomers lead to the formation of different organic products. Determine the structures of the organic products formed from the oxidation of each alcohol isomer in (c) (i) above and list the conditions required to obtain the different products. [5]

Paper 3

Option A — Modern analytical chemistry

A1. State **two** reasons for the use of analytical techniques in today's society. *[2]*

A2. A student analyses the amount of Cu^{2+} in a water sample using atomic absorption spectroscopy. A simplified diagram of the atomic absorption spectrophotometer is shown below.

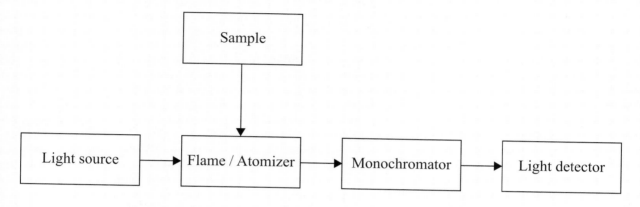

(a) State the essential characteristic of the lamp providing the light source. *[1]*

(b) Describe what happens to the Cu^{2+} (aq) ions when introduced into the atomizer. *[2]*

(c) Describe the function of the monochromator. *[1]*

(d) Explain how the student can determine the concentration of Cu^{2+} (aq) ions in the water sample using an atomic absorption spectrophotometer and a solution of $0.10\ mol\,dm^{-3}$ $CuSO_4$. *[4]*

A3. Paper chromatography may be used to separate a mixture of sugars.

(a) State the stationary phase and an example of a mobile phase used in paper chromatography. *[2]*

Stationary phase:

Mobile phase:

(This question continues on the following page)

(Question A3 continued)

(b) The identity of two sugars in a mixture can be determined by measuring their R_f values, after staining.

      (i) Describe how an R_f value can be calculated.   *[1]*

      (ii) Calculate the R_f value for sugar 2 in the chromatogram below.   *[1]*

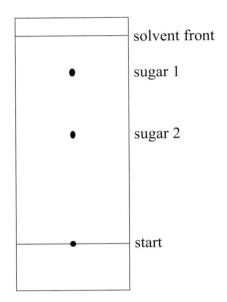

(c) Explain how the R_f value of sugar 2 could be used to identify it.   *[2]*

A4. (a) Explain why the nitrogen molecule, N_2, does not absorb infrared radiation.   *[2]*

    (b) Describe **two** vibrations in the water molecule that absorb infrared radiation.   *[2]*

Option B — Human biochemistry

B1. The energy value of food may be determined using a food calorimeter.

The combustion of 2.00 g of dried bread in a food calorimeter raised the temperature of 600 cm^3 water from 20.5 °C to 29.0 °C. Calculate the energy content of bread in kJ per 100 g. Specific heat capacity of water = 4.18 J g^{-1} K^{-1}.

[4]

B2. Proteins are natural polymers.

   (a) List **four** major functions of proteins in the human body.

[2]

   (b) Deduce the structures of **two** different tripeptides that can be formed when all three amino acids given below react together.

[2]

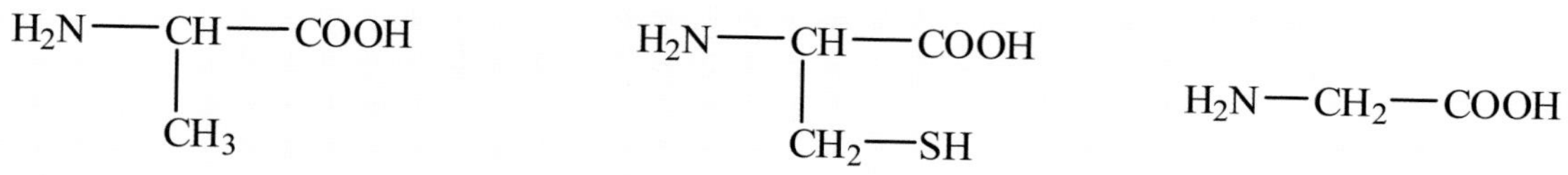

$$H_2N—CH—COOH \qquad H_2N—CH—COOH \qquad H_2N—CH_2—COOH$$
$$\quad\;\; | \qquad\qquad\qquad\qquad\;\; | $$
$$\quad\;\; CH_3 \qquad\qquad\qquad\qquad CH_2—SH$$

   (c) Deduce the number of tripeptides that could be formed by using all three of the above amino acids to form a tripeptide.

[1]

   (d) State the type of bonding that is responsible for the primary and secondary structures of proteins.

[2]

      Primary:

      Secondary:

   (e) Describe and explain the tertiary structure of proteins. Include in your answer all the bonds and interactions responsible for the tertiary structure.

[2]

B3. (a) State what is meant by the term *dietary fibre*.

[1]

   (b) Describe the importance of a high fibre diet and list **two** health problems related to a low fibre diet.

[2]

B4. Hormones play an important role in the body.

   (a) Outline the function and production of hormones in the body.

[2]

   (b) In many communities there are people who use steroids appropriately, and others who abuse them. Outline **one** appropriate use and **one** abuse of steroids.

[2]

Option C — Chemistry in industry and technology

C1. Nanotechnology creates and uses structures that have novel properties because of their size.

  (a) State the size range of structures which are involved in nanotechnology.   *[1]*

  (b) Distinguish between physical and chemical techniques in manipulating atoms to form molecules.   *[2]*

  (c) Discuss **two** implications of nanotechnology.   *[2]*

C2. The blast furnace is used extensively for the production of iron.

  (a) State the formula and name of **one** main ore used as a source of iron.   *[1]*

  (b) Write an equation that would describe the following processes in the blast furnace.

   (i)   Reduction of the iron ore to produce the iron: *[1]*

   (ii) A reaction used to remove impurities from the iron: *[1]*

C3. Addition polymers are extensively used in society. The properties of addition polymers may be modified by the introduction of certain substances.

  (a) For two different addition polymers, describe and explain **one** way in which the properties of addition polymers may be modified.   *[4]*

   Polymer one:

   Polymer two:

  (b) Describe and explain how the extent of branching affects the properties of poly(ethene).   *[3]*

  (c) Discuss **two** advantages and **two** disadvantages of using poly(ethene).   *[2]*

C4. Detergents are one example of lyotropic liquid crystals.

  State **one** other example of a lyotropic liquid crystal and describe the difference between lyotropic and thermotropic liquid crystals.   *[3]*

Option D — Medicines and drugs

D1. State the differences between the structures of morphine and diamorphine (heroin). State the names of all functional groups in the molecule of morphine. *[3]*

Differences:

Functional groups:

D2. Bacterial and viral infections require different types of medication.

    (a)   Outline **two** differences between bacteria and viruses. *[2]*

    (b)   Antiviral drugs are used for the treatment of HIV and other viral infections. Describe **two** ways in which antiviral drugs work. *[2]*

    (c)   Discuss why viral infections are generally harder to treat than bacterial infections. *[3]*

D3. Mild analgesics such as aspirin, and strong analgesics such as opiates, differ not only in their potency but also in the ways they act on the central nervous system.

    (a)   Describe how mild and strong analgesics provide pain relief. *[2]*

        Mild analgesics:

        Strong analgesics:

    (b)   Discuss **two** advantages and **two** disadvantages of using morphine and other opiates for pain relief. *[4]*

        Advantages:

        Disadvantages:

D4. Fluoxetine hydrochloride (Prozac®) is a common depressant. Depressants have many therapeutic uses.

    (a)   State **three** other common depressants. *[3]*

    (b)   Describe **one** effect, other than relieving depression, of moderate doses of depressants on patients. *[1]*

Option E — Environmental chemistry

E1. The greenhouse effect maintains the Earth's average temperature at a habitable level. The components of the Earth's atmosphere responsible for this effect are called greenhouse gases.

    (a)   Major greenhouse gases are water vapour and carbon dioxide. State **two** other greenhouse gases. *[2]*

    (b)   Describe how greenhouse gases cause the greenhouse effect. *[3]*

    (c)   Discuss **three** possible implications of global warming on world food production. *[3]*

E2. Disposal of radioactive waste is a major ecological concern.

    (a)   State **one** source of low-level radioactive waste and **one** source of high-level radioactive waste. *[2]*

    Low-level waste:

    High-level waste:

    (b)   Consider the following types of radioactive waste.

Type	Waste	Isotopes	Half-life	Emissions
A	syringes and other disposable materials used in radiotherapy	^{90}Y	64 hours	β^-
B	diluted aqueous solution of cobalt-60 complexes	^{60}Co	5.3 years	β^-, γ
C	partially processed solid materials from a nuclear reactor	U, Pu, Am and other actinides	10^3–10^9 years	α, γ

    Identify which method can be used for the disposal of radioactive wastes **A**, **B** and **C**.

    (i)   Vitrification followed by long-term underground storage: *[1]*

    (ii)   Storage in a non-shielded container for two months followed by the disposal as normal (non-radioactive) waste: *[1]*

    (iii)   Ion-exchange and adsorption on iron(II) hydroxide, storage in a shielded container for 50 years, then mixing with concrete and shallow land burial: *[1]*

E3. The ozone layer protects living organisms from dangerous UV radiation. In the Earth's stratosphere, ozone is photochemically formed from oxygen by the following two-step process.

$$O_2 \xrightarrow{\text{UV light}} 2O\bullet$$
$$O_2 + O\bullet \longrightarrow O_3$$

(a) Ozone decomposition can proceed photochemically. Describe, using chemical equations, the two-step mechanism of photochemical decomposition of ozone in the Earth's stratosphere. *[2]*

Step 1:

Step 2:

(b) Ozone decomposition can also be catalysed by ozone-depleting substances such as chlorofluorocarbons, CFCs. State **two** alternatives to CFCs. *[1]*

E4. Intensive farming changes the composition of soils and may lead to soil degradation. Common types of soil degradation include *salinization*, *nutrient depletion* and *soil pollution*.

Discuss **two** types of soil degradation. In your answer you should describe how each type of soil degradation occurs and suggest **one** negative effect on the environment. *[4]*

Option F — Food chemistry

F1. The preservation of food is important around the world.

    (a)   Explain the meaning of the term *shelf life*.   *[2]*

    (b)   Discuss **two** factors that can affect the shelf life of food.   *[4]*

F2. (a)   Describe the differences in the structure between the saturated fatty acid $C_{16}H_{32}O_2$ and the unsaturated fatty acid $C_{16}H_{26}O_2$.   *[3]*

    (b)   Describe how $C_{16}H_{26}O_2$ can be converted to $C_{16}H_{32}O_2$.   *[3]*

    (c)   Fatty acids are components of fats and oils.

        (i)   Describe **one** advantage of the products formed by hydrogenating fats and oils.   *[1]*

        (ii)   Describe **one** disadvantage of the products formed by hydrogenating fats and oils.   *[1]*

F3. (a)   Define the term *antioxidant* and state its use.   *[2]*

    (b)   Discuss **one** disadvantage of using natural and synthetic antioxidants.   *[2]*

        Natural antioxidants:

        Synthetic antioxidants:

F4. Flavanones are pigments that produce a red colouration. Distinguish between a pigment and a dye.   *[2]*

Option G — Further organic chemistry

G1. Addition of hydrogen halides to unsymmetrical alkenes produces a mixture of halogenoalkanes. The latter can be converted into Grignard reagents by reaction with magnesium metal and then used for the preparation of various organic molecules with an increased number of carbon atoms.

(a) State in the boxes below, the formulas of the organic substances needed to complete the following reaction pathways. *[4]*

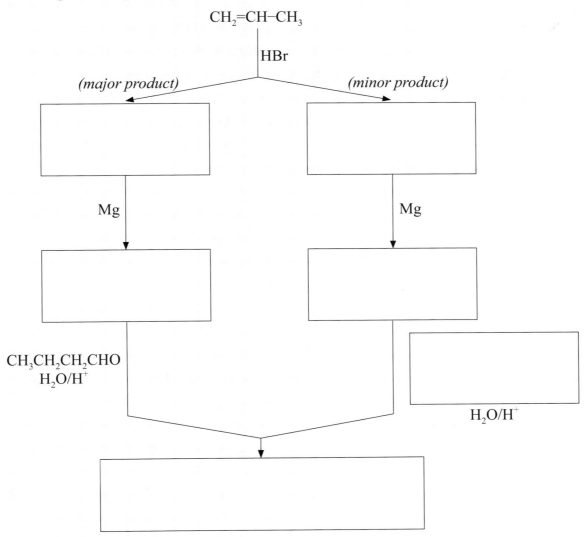

(b) Describe, using equations and curly arrows to represent the movement of electron pairs, the mechanism of the reaction between propene and hydrogen bromide. Compare the relative stabilities of the two intermediate carbocations which lead to the formation of the major and minor products. *[4]*

G2. Hydrolysis of aliphatic and aromatic halides occurs under different conditions.

State an equation, using structural formulas, to show the reaction of 1-chloro-2-(chloromethyl) benzene with excess sodium hydroxide at room temperature. *[2]*

G3. Deduce a **two-step** reaction pathway for the conversion of butan-1-ol into 1,2-dibromobutane. State the appropriate equations, the reaction conditions and the reaction type for each step.   *[5]*

Step 1:

Reaction type for step 1:

Step 2:

Reaction type for step 2:

G4. The acidity of carboxylic acids depends on the carbon chain length and the nature of substituents in their molecules. Table 15 of the Data Booklet provides some examples.

(a) State and explain how the presence of halogen atoms in the hydrocarbon chain affects the acidity of carboxylic acids.   *[3]*

(b) State how the acidity of 3-chloropropanoic acid compares to that of propanoic acid and chloroethanoic acid.   *[1]*

(c) Suggest the pK_a value for 3-chloropropanoic acid.   *[1]*

Notes

Also from the IB store...

International Baccalaureate
Baccalauréat International
Bachillerato Internacional

Other subjects in the *IB Prepared* series

Group 3

Economics SL · Economics HL

Business and management SL · Business and management HL

Group 4

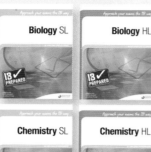

Biology SL · Biology HL · Physics SL

Chemistry SL · Chemistry HL · Physics HL

Group 5

Mathematics SL · Mathematical studies SL

Mathematics HL

Core requirements

Extended essay

Theory of knowledge

Sign up to receive the IB store eNewsletter and hear about new subjects as they are added to this series

You may also be interested in... *IB Questionbank* series

Group 2
French B · Spanish B

Group 3
Question bank — Business and management · Question bank — Environmental systems and societies

Group 4
Question bank — Biology Second edition · Question bank — Chemistry Second edition · Question bank — Physics Second edition

Group 5
Question bank — Mathematics Second edition

Sign up to receive the IB store eNewsletter and hear about new subjects as they are added to this series

Get involved!

We welcome feedback on existing publications and any suggestions for new publications to complement IB programme materials:

- **Leave a review** on the relevant product page on the IB store
- **Send ideas and suggestions** for new resources to publishing.proposals@ibo.org

New publication alert/ eNewsletter sign-up

Visit the IB store to sign up for new publication alerts or to receive our quarterly eNewsletter.

Discounts

The more copies you buy the more you save —volume discounts now available on selected products

Stationery items and accessories

 Duo highlighter pen multipack

 Flower highlighter

 Laptop sleeve

 Baseball cap

For more items like these, go to the **Gift items** area of the IB store.

Downloads

Did you know that individual exam papers are available to buy on the IB store? To find exam papers for your subject area, go to the IB store at **http://store.ibo.org** > **Diploma Programme (DP)** > **Examinations, reports & markschemes.**

Many of our publications have sample chapters/pages available to download for free. See the product page on the IB store for details.

To make a purchase or for further information about IB products, prices and services, please visit the IB store at **http://store.ibo.org** or contact the IB store team at **sales@ibo.org**.

* Publication dates are correct at time of going to press.
© International Baccalaureate Organization 2011